Working Papers

for use with

Fundamental ACCOUNTING PRINCIPLES

Volume 2

FIFTEENTH CANADIAN EDITION

Revised by Laura Dallas

and reviewed by Michelle Young

McGraw Hill Education

Working Papers

for use with

undamental
CCOUNTING PRINCIPLES

Volume 2

FIFTEENTH CANADIAN EDITION

Kermit D. Larson
University of Texas—Austin

Tilly Jensen
Athabasca University—Alberta

Heidi Dieckmann
Kwantlen Polytechnic University—British Columbia

Revised by Laura Dallas

and reviewed by Michelle Young

Mc
Graw
Hill
Education

Working Papers for use with
Fundamental Accounting Principles
Fifteenth Canadian Edition
Volume 2

ISBN-13: 978-1-25-910576-0
ISBN-10: 1-25-910576-8

4 5 6 7 8 9 MP 22 21 20 19 18

Printed and bound in Canada.

Care has been taken to trace ownership of copyright material contained in this text; however, the publisher will welcome any information that enables them to rectify any reference or credit for subsequent editions.

Director of Product Management: Rhondda McNabb
Product Manager: Keara Emmett
Executive Marketing Manager: Joy Armitage Taylor
Product Developer: Sarah Fulton
Supervising Editor: Jessica Barnoski
Plant Production Coordinator: Scott Morrison
Manufacturing Production Coordinator: Emily Hickey
Cover Design: Michelle Losier
Cover Image: Rachel Idzerda
Page Layout: Aptara®, Inc.
Printer: Maracle Press, Ltd.

Contents

$18,000 + 180,000 + 3,000 + 600 = \$201,600$

Quick Study 9-2

(1)

(a) expense   (c) expense

(b) Capital   (d) capital

(2)

GENERAL JOURNAL   Page____

Date	Account Titles and Explanation	PR	Debit	Credit
mar 15	maintenance expense		120	
	Accounts Payable			120
	Refrigeratio Equipment		40,000	
	Accounts Payable			40,000
	Repairs Expense		200	
	Accounts Payable			200
	Office Building		175,000	
	Accounts Payable			175,000

Quick Study 9-3

PPE Item	(a) Appraised Values	(b) Ratio of Individual Appraised Value to Total Appraised Value (a) ÷ Total Appraised Value	(c) Cost Allocation (b) × Total Actual Cost
Land	$320,000	320,000 ÷ 500,000 = 64%	345,600
Building	180,000	180,000 ÷ 500,000 = 36%	194,000
Totals	$500,000		$540,000

GENERAL JOURNAL

Date	Account Titles and Explanation	PR	Debit	Credit
	Land		345,000	
	Building		194,400	
	Cash			85,000
	Notes Payable			455,000

Quick Study 9-4

TechCom
Partial Balance Sheet
October 31, 2017

Assets:			
Current Assets:			
Cash		$9,000	
Accounts Receivable	$16,400		
Less: Allowance for Doubtful Accounts	800	15,600	
Total current assets			$24,600
Property, Plant equipment:			
Land		48,000	
Vehicles	62,000		
Less: Accumulated depreciation	13,800	48,200	
Equipment	25,000		
Less: Accumulated depreciation	3,800	21,200	
Total property, plant, equipment			117,400
Intangible Assets			
Patent	20,100		
Less: Accumulated Amortization patent	3,100		17,000
			$159,000

Quick Study 9-5   ($55,900 − 1,900)/4 = $13,500 per year

Rate per copy = ($45,000 − 5,000)/4,000,000 copies = .01¢ per copy

Year	Calculation		Annual Depreciation
2017	.01 * 650,000	=	$6,500
2018	.01 * 798,000	=	7,980
2019	.01 * 424,000	=	4,240
2020	.01 * 935,000	=	9,350
2021	.01 * 1,193,000	=	11,930
Total			$40,000

Quick Study 9-7

86,000 − 16,000 -   Annual rate of depreciation = 2/5 years = 40% per year

Year	Calculation	Annual Depreciation
2017	40% of 86,000	$34,400
2018	40% of (86,000−34,400) =	$20,640
2019	40% of (86,000−34,400−20,640) =	$12,384
2020	40% of (86,000−34,400−20,640−12,384) =	$2,576
2021		0
Total		$70,000

Quick Study 9-8

a) 4000/8 years = 500 a year

b) 70,000 − 5000/400,000 garment = .1625 per garment
    .1625 * 62,000 garments = $10,075 depreciation

c) 85,000 − 10,000 = 75 000/20 years = 3750 depreciation

d)

Name _____

a. _____

_____

_____

b. _____

_____

_____

Quick Study 9-10

a. _____

_____

_____

b. _____

_____

_____

Quick Study 9-11

a. _____

_____

_____

b. _____

_____

_____

Quick Study 9-12

_____

_____

_____

_____

_____

_____

_____

GENERAL JOURNAL   Page____

Date	Account Titles and Explanation	PR	Debit	Credit

Calculations: _____
_____
_____
_____
_____
_____
_____
_____
_____
_____
_____

Quick Study 9-14

_____
_____
_____
_____
_____

Calculations:

Asset	Cost	Accumulated Depreciation	Book Value	Recoverable Amount	Impairment Loss
Building	$1,200,000	$465,000		$735,000	
Computer	3,500	1,800		200	
Furniture	79,000	53,000		5,000	
Land	630,000	0		790,000	
Machine	284,000	117,000		172,000	

a. **GENERAL JOURNAL** Page____

Date	Account Titles and Explanation	PR	Debit	Credit

b. **GENERAL JOURNAL** Page____

Date	Account Titles and Explanation	PR	Debit	Credit

c. **GENERAL JOURNAL** Page____

Date	Account Titles and Explanation	PR	Debit	Credit

d. **GENERAL JOURNAL** Page____

Date	Account Titles and Explanation	PR	Debit	Credit

Chapter 9   Quick Study 9-16   *Name* _____

GENERAL JOURNAL   Page____

Date	Account Titles and Explanation	PR	Debit	Credit

Calculations: _____
_____
_____
_____
_____

Quick Study 9-17

GENERAL JOURNAL   Page____

Date	Account Titles and Explanation	PR	Debit	Credit

Calculations: _____
_____
_____
_____
_____

GENERAL JOURNAL   Page____

Date	Account Titles and Explanation	PR	Debit	Credit

Quick Study 9-19

GENERAL JOURNAL   Page____

Date	Account Titles and Explanation	PR	Debit	Credit

Calculations:
_____
_____
_____
_____
_____
_____

	Calculation	
Motor (old)		
Motor (new)		
Metal housing		
Misc. parts		
Total depreciation expense to be recorded on the machine for 2017 =		

Exercise 9-1

Invoice Cost	$15,000
Freight costs	260
Steel mounting	795
Assembly	375
Raw materials for testing	120
less: discount ($15000 * 8%)	300
Total aquisition Costs	$16,250

Note: The 190 repairs are an expense and therefor not capitalized.

Chapter 9 Exercise 9-2   *Name* _____

Cost of land:

Purchase Price of Land	1,200,000
Purchase Price for old building	480,000
Demo costs for old building	75,000
Leveling the lot	105,000
Total cost of land	$1,860,000

Cost of building:

Construction Costs	2,880,000
Less: Cost of land improvements	- 215,000
Cost of new building	$2,665,000

The land improvements are a distinct PPE Assets
That depreciates at a different than the land

Journal entry:

GENERAL JOURNAL   Page____

Date	Account Titles and Explanation	PR	Debit	Credit
2017	Land		1,860,000	
mar 10	Land Improvements		215,000	
	Building		2,665,000	
	Cash			4,740,000
	To record cost of			
	plant asset			

Name _____

PPE Asset	(a) Appraised Values	(b) Ratio of Individual Appraised Value to Total Appraised Value (a) ÷ Total Appraised Value	(c) Cost Allocation (b) × Total Actual Cost
Land	249,248 ÷ 594,000 = 42%		$244,346
Land Imp.	83,160 ÷ 594,000 = 14%		$ 81,448
Building	261,360 ÷ 594,000 = 44%		$255,981
Totals	594,000		$581,775

Journal entry:

GENERAL JOURNAL   Page_____

Date	Account Titles and Explanation	PR	Debit	Credit

GENERAL JOURNAL   Page____

Date	Account Titles and Explanation	PR	Debit	Credit
2017	Land		1,296,000	
Jan 1	Building		1,512,000	
	Equipment		1,123,000	
	Tools		388,800	
	Cash			1,104,000
	Notes Payable			3,216,000
	To record lumpsum			
	Purchase			

Calculations:

PPE Asset	(a) Appraised Values	(b) Ratio of Individual Appraised Value to Total Appraised Value (a) ÷ Total Appraised Value	(c) Cost Allocation (b) × Total Actual Cost
Land	1,152,000 ÷	3,840,000 = 30%	$1,296,000
Building	1,344,000 ÷	3,840,000 = 35%	$1,512,000
Equip.	998,400 ÷	3,840,000 = 26%	$1,123,200
Tools	345,600 ÷	3,840,000 = 9%	$ 388,800
Totals	3,840,000		$4,320,000

Name _____

GENERAL JOURNAL

Page____

Date		Account Titles and Explanation	PR	Debit	Credit
2017		Truck		63,000	
Jan	1	Cash			63,000
		37,500 + 13,500 + 6,750 + 5250 = 63,000			
Jan	4	Prepaid Insurance		3,600	
		Gas expense		180	
		Cash			3,780
2017		depreciation expense, truck		11,100	
dec	31	Accum. depreciation Truck			11,100
		To record depreciation			

Calculations: [(37,500 + 13,500 + 6750 + 5250) − 7500] / 5years = 11,100

_____

_____

_____

_____

_____

_____

Year	Straight-Line
2017	36,300
2018	36,300
2019	36,300
2020	36,300

Year	Double-Declining-Balance (Rate= 2/4 = 50%
2017	50% * 169,200 = 84,600 .
2018	50% * (169,200 - 84,600) = 42300
2019	18,300
2020	0

Year	Units-of-Production
2017	30,640 (.80 * 38 300)
2018	32,920 (.80 * 41 150)
2019	42,080 (.80 * 52,600)
2020	39,560

Rate = [(169,200 - 24,000)/181,500] = .80/unit

Exercise 9-7

a. (238,400 - 46,400)/5 = 38,400

b. Rate = 2/5 = 40%
   40% * 238,400 = $95 360

c. Rate = (238,400 - 46,400)/240 000 km = .80/km
   .80/km * 38,000 km = 30,400

Analysis component:

_____
_____
_____
_____
_____
_____
_____
_____
_____
_____

Year	Straight-Line Method	
	Depreciation Expense	**Book Value at December 31**
2017		
2018		
2019		
2020		
2021		

Year	Double-Declining Balance Method	
	Depreciation Expense	**Book Value at December 31**
2017		
2018		
2019		
2020		
2021		

Year	Units-of-Production Method	
	Depreciation Expense	**Book Value at December 31**
2017		
2018		
2019		
2020		
2021		

Analysis component: _____

a. _____

_____

b. _____

_____

Chapter 9   Exercise 9-9   *Name* _____

Step 1: Cost allocation

PPE Asset	(a) Appraised Values	(b) Ratio of Individual Appraised Value to Total Appraised Value *(a) ÷ Total Appraised Value*	(c) Cost Allocation *(b) × Total Actual Cost*
Land			
Building			
Equip.			
Tools			
Totals	_____		_____

Step 2: Calculate depreciation

PPE asset	Cost (from c above)	2017 Depreciation	2018 Depreciation
Land			
Building			
Equip.			
Tools			

Analysis component: _____
_____
_____
_____
_____
_____
_____

Name _____

| | | Cost Information | | | | | Depreciation | | |
Description	Date of Purchase	Depreciation Method	Cost	Residual Value	Life	Balance of Accum. Deprec. Dec. 31, 2016	Balance of Accum. Deprec. Dec. 31, 2016	Depreciation Expense for 2017	Balance of Accum. Deprec. Dec. 31, 2017
Modular Building	May 2, 2011	S/L	$650,000	$250,000	10 yr.	$226,667			
Furniture	May 2, 2011	S/L	72,000	0	6 yr.	68,000			
Truck	January 25, 2014	DDB	80,000	10,000	8 yr.	45,313			

Analysis component:

_____

_____

_____

_____

_____

_____

Name _____

Dynamic Exploration
Partial Balance Sheet
December 31, 2016

Exercise 9-12

a. Straight-line

	Year 1	Year 2	Year 3	Year 4	Year 5	5-Year Totals
Profit before deprec.						
Deprec. expense						
Profit						

b. Double-declining-balance

	Year 1	Year 2	Year 3	Year 4	Year 5	5-Year Totals
Profit before deprec.						
Deprec. expense						
Profit (loss)						

Analysis component:

_____
_____
_____
_____
_____
_____

(handwritten, upper right) $\frac{Cost - RV}{life}$

| Year | Depreciation | |
	Straight-Line	Units-of-Production
2017		
2018		
2019		

Analysis component: _____
_____
_____
_____

Exercise 9-14

| Year | Depreciation | |
	Straight-Line	Double-Declining-Balance
2017		
2018		
2019		

Analysis component: _____
_____
_____
_____

Exercise 9-15

Year	(a) Straight-line	(b) Double-declining balance
2017		
2018		

Cost – RV
—————
life

1. $43,500 - 5,000 = 9,625$ per year x 2 years = 19,250 Acc dep
   (over 4)

   Book value = $43,500 - 19,250 = 24,250$

2. $(43,500 - 19,250) - 3850 / 3 = 6,800$

_____

_____

Exercise 9-17

GENERAL JOURNAL   Page____

Date		Account Titles and Explanation	PR	Debit	Credit
2020 Dec	31	depreciation exp.		7624	
		accum. depreciation			7624

Calculations:

$$\frac{71,200 - 15,200}{5} = 11,200 * \frac{9}{12} = year 1 \ \$8,400$$

2017   8,400
2018   11,200
2019   11,200
          30,800

          71 200
        - 30 800
          40 400

$$\frac{40 400 - 8,000}{4.25} = \$7,624 \ per \ year$$

Chapter 9 Exercise 9-18

Name _____

Part 1

GENERAL JOURNAL

Page____

Date	Account Titles and Explanation	PR	Debit	Credit
2017	Warehouse-door		25,500	
Jan 5	Accounts Payable			25,500
	To record addition of			
	door on east-wall of			
	Ware house			

Part 2

GENERAL JOURNAL

Page____

Date	Account Titles and Explanation	PR	Debit	Credit
	depreciation exp.-Warehouse		14 700	
	accum. depreciation-Warehouse			14 700
	Total depreciation on			
	Warehouse			

Exercise 9-19 $\dfrac{292\ 500 - 30{,}000}{15} = \$13\ 500 + \dfrac{25\ 500 - 7500}{5} = \$1200$

Part 1

GENERAL JOURNAL

Page____

Date	Account Titles and Explanation	PR	Debit	Credit

Part 2

GENERAL JOURNAL

Page____

Date	Account Titles and Explanation	PR	Debit	Credit

GENERAL JOURNAL   Page____

Date	Account Titles and Explanation	PR	Debit	Credit

Calculations:

Asset	Cost	Accum. Deprec.	Book Value	Recoverable Amount	Impairment Loss	2018 Dep. Exp.
Equipment	$40,000	$20,000		$ 8,000		
Furniture	12,000	9,509		2,950		
Land	85,000	N/A		101,800		
Office Bldng	77,000	23,000		52,500		
Warehouse	55,000	12,938		45,100		

respondus

Chapter 9   Exercise 9-20

Name _____

a.

| | GENERAL JOURNAL | | | Page____ |

Date	Account Titles and Explanation	PR	Debit	Credit
2017	Accum. depreciation truck		21 850	
mar 1	cash		20 150	
	Truck			42,000
	To record sale of truck			

b.

| | GENERAL JOURNAL | | | Page____ |

Date	Account Titles and Explanation	PR	Debit	Credit
Mar 1	Accum. depreciation Truck		21850	
	cash		21 850	
	Truck			42,000
	Gain on disposal			1,450
	To record sale of truck			
	for 21 850			

c.

| | GENERAL JOURNAL | | | Page____ |

Date	Account Titles and Explanation	PR	Debit	Credit
mar 1	Accum. depreciation-truck		21 850	
	cash		19 200	
	Loss on disposal		950	
	Truck			42,000
	To record sale of truck			
	for 19 200			

d.

| | GENERAL JOURNAL | | | Page____ |

Date	Account Titles and Explanation	PR	Debit	Credit
	Accum depreciation - Truck		21,850	
	Loss on disposal		20,150	
	Truck			42,000
	To record sale of truck			
	for $0; it was scrapped			

Copyright © 2016 McGraw-Hill Education Limited. All rights reserved.

Fundamental Accounting Principles, 15ce, Working Papers   23

To record partial year's depreciation in 2021:

GENERAL JOURNAL   Page____

Date	Account Titles and Explanation	PR	Debit	Credit

a.   GENERAL JOURNAL   Page____

Date	Account Titles and Explanation	PR	Debit	Credit

b.   GENERAL JOURNAL   Page____

Date	Account Titles and Explanation	PR	Debit	Credit

1. _____
   _____

2. _____
   _____
   _____
   _____
   _____

3. _____
   _____

4.

GENERAL JOURNAL   Page____

Date		Account Titles and Explanation	PR	Debit	Credit

GENERAL JOURNAL   Page____

Date	Account Titles and Explanation	PR	Debit	Credit
a.				
b.				

Analysis component:

_____

_____

_____

_____

_____

_____

Name _____

GENERAL JOURNAL

Page_____

Date		Account Titles and Explanation	PR	Debit	Credit
a.					
b.					
c.					
d.					

Exercise 9-25

GENERAL JOURNAL

Page_____

Date		Account Titles and Explanation	PR	Debit	Credit
2017		Copy rights		177,480	
Jan	1	cash			177,480
		to record purchase			
dec	31	Amort. exp. copyrights		14,790	
		accum. depreciation			14,790

Name _____

GENERAL JOURNAL   Page____

Date	Account Titles and Explanation	PR	Debit	Credit
Part 1.				
Part 2.				

Name _____

_____
_____

Name _____

Name _____

GENERAL JOURNAL   Page____

Date	Account Titles and Explanation	PR	Debit	Credit

Name _____

Part 1   GENERAL JOURNAL   Page____

Date	Account Titles and Explanation	PR	Debit	Credit

Part 2: _____

_____

_____

_____

_____

_____

_____

_____

_____

_____

_____

_____

_____

_____

_____

_____

_____

_____

Part 3: _____

_____

_____

_____

_____

_____

_____

Part 1

	Land	Building Two	Building Three	Land Improv. One	Land Improv. Two
Purchase price					
Demolition					
Landscaping					
New building					
New improvements ..					
Totals					

Calculations:

	Appraised Value	Percent of Total	Apportioned Cost
Land			
Building Two			
Land Improvements One			
Totals			

Part 2

GENERAL JOURNAL   Page____

Date	Account Titles and Explanation	PR	Debit	Credit

Name _____

Derlak Enterprises
Balance Sheet
December 31

	2017		2016	

Fundamental Accounting Principles, 15ce, Working Papers

Analysis component:

_____
_____
_____
_____
_____
_____
_____
_____

Problem 9-3A

Part 1 Purchased January 1, 2017

	2017	2018	2019
A. Double-declining-balance method			
Equipment	$375,000	$375,000	$375,000
Less: Accumulated depreciation			
Year-end book value			
Depreciation expense for the year			
B. Straight-line method			
Equipment	$375,000	$375,000	$375,000
Less: Accumulated depreciation			
Year-end book value			
Depreciation expense for the year			

Calculations:

_____
_____
_____
_____
_____
_____
_____
_____

Part 2 Purchased July 1, 2017

	2017	2018	2019
A. Double-declining-balance method			
Equipment	$375,000	$375,000	$375,000
Less: Accumulated depreciation			
Year-end book value			
Depreciation expense for the year			
B. Straight-line method			
Equipment	$375,000	$375,000	$375,000
Less: Accumulated depreciation			
Year-end book value			
Depreciation expense for the year			

Calculations: _____

_____

_____

_____

_____

_____

_____

_____

Name _____

Year	Depreciation Method		
	Straight-Line	Double-Declining-Balance	Units-of-Production
2017			
2018			
2019			

Analysis component:

_____
_____
_____
_____
_____
_____
_____
_____
_____
_____

Name

Year	Depreciation Method:		
	Straight-line	**Double-declining balance**	**Units-of-production**
2017			
2018			
2019			

Calculations:

1. **Double-declining-balance method**
   <u>**2017**</u>   <u>**2018**</u>   <u>**2019**</u>

   Equipment .... _____

   Less: Accumulated depreciation .... _____

   Year-end book value .... _____

   Depreciation expense for the year .... _____

2. **Straight-line method**
   <u>**2017**</u>   <u>**2018**</u>   <u>**2019**</u>

   Equipment .... _____

   Less: Accumulated depreciation .... _____

   Year-end book value .... _____

   Depreciation expense for the year ...... _____

Part 1

GENERAL JOURNAL   Page____

Date	Account Titles and Explanation	PR	Debit	Credit

Part 2

BigSky Farms
Partial Balance Sheet
April 30, 2018

Chapter 9   Problem 9-7A

Part 1

	Market Value	Percentage of Total	Apportioned Cost
Building			
Land			
Land improvements			
Vehicles			
Total			

GENERAL JOURNAL

Page____

Date	Account Titles and Explanation	PR	Debit	Credit

Part 2: 2017 straight-line depreciation on building:

Part 3: 2017 double-declining-balance depreciation on land improvements:

Analysis component:

Name _____

Year	Depreciation		
	Straight-Line	Units-of-Production	Double-Declining-Balance
2017			
2018			
2019			
2020			
2021			
Totals			

Calculations:

	Cost Information					Balance of Accum. Deprec. Dec. 31, 2017	Depreciation	
							Depreciation Expense for 2018	Balance of Accum. Deprec. Dec. 31, 2018
Description	Date of Purchase	Depreciation Method	Cost	Residual	Life			
Office equipment	March 27/14	Straight-line	$52,000	$14,000	10 yr.			
Machinery	June 4/14	Double-declining-balance	275,000	46,000	6 yr.			
Truck	Nov. 13/17	Units-of-production	113,000	26,000	250,000 km.			

Calculations:

Name _____

GENERAL JOURNAL

Page_____

Date	Account Titles and Explanation	PR	Debit	Credit

Calculations:

GENERAL JOURNAL

Page____

Date		Account Titles and Explanation	PR	Debit	Credit

Calculations:

Part 1: Entry to record the purchase of the replacement blade:

GENERAL JOURNAL   Page____

Date	Account Titles and Explanation	PR	Debit	Credit

Calculations:

Part 2: Total depreciation expense to be recorded on Machine #5027 for 2017:_____

Calculations:

Part 1   **GENERAL JOURNAL**   Page____

Date	Account Titles and Explanation	PR	Debit	Credit

Calculations:

Analysis component:

_____
_____
_____
_____
_____
_____
_____
_____
_____
_____
_____
_____

Problem 9-14A

Part 1   **GENERAL JOURNAL**   Page____

Date	Account Titles and Explanation	PR	Debit	Credit

Calculations:

Part 2   **GENERAL JOURNAL**   Page____

Date	Account Titles and Explanation	PR	Debit	Credit

Calculations:

Name _____

Part 1   GENERAL JOURNAL   Page____

Date	Account Titles and Explanation	PR	Debit	Credit

Part 2   GENERAL JOURNAL   Page____

Date	Account Titles and Explanation	PR	Debit	Credit

Part 3(a)   GENERAL JOURNAL   Page____

Date	Account Titles and Explanation	PR	Debit	Credit

Part 3(b)   GENERAL JOURNAL   Page____

Date	Account Titles and Explanation	PR	Debit	Credit

Part 3(c)   GENERAL JOURNAL   Page____

Date	Account Titles and Explanation	PR	Debit	Credit

Calculations:

GENERAL JOURNAL   Page____

Date	Account Titles and Explanation	PR	Debit	Credit

Calculations:

a. Depreciation expense on first December 31 of each machine's life:

GENERAL JOURNAL   Page____

Date	Account Titles and Explanation	PR	Debit	Credit

b. Purchase/exchange/disposal of each machine:

GENERAL JOURNAL   Page____

Date	Account Titles and Explanation	PR	Debit	Credit

GENERAL JOURNAL

Date		Account Titles and Explanation	PR	Debit	Credit

Calculations:

a.   **GENERAL JOURNAL**   Page____

Date	Account Titles and Explanation	PR	Debit	Credit

b.   **GENERAL JOURNAL**   Page____

Date	Account Titles and Explanation	PR	Debit	Credit

Problem 9-19A

Part 1   **GENERAL JOURNAL**   Page____

Date	Account Titles and Explanation	PR	Debit	Credit

Part 2   **GENERAL JOURNAL**   Page____

Date	Account Titles and Explanation	PR	Debit	Credit

a.   GENERAL JOURNAL   Page____

Date	Account Titles and Explanation	PR	Debit	Credit

b.   GENERAL JOURNAL   Page____

Date	Account Titles and Explanation	PR	Debit	Credit

Calculations:

Part 2

_____
_____
_____
_____
_____
_____
_____

Name _____

Part 1

	Land	Building B	Building C	Land Improv. B	Land Improv. C
Purchase price					
Demolition					
Landscaping					
New building					
New improvements ...	_____	_____	_____	_____	_____
Totals					

Calculations:

Allocation of purchase price:

	Appraised Value	*Percent of Total*	*Apportioned Cost*
Land	$317,034		
Building B	189,108		
Land Improvements B	50,058		
Totals	$556,200	100 %	$540,000

Part 2

GENERAL JOURNAL   Page_____

Date		Account Titles and Explanation	PR	Debit	Credit

Fundamental Accounting Principles, 15ce, Working Papers

	2017		2016	

Xentel Interactive
Balance Sheet
September 30

Analysis component:

_____

_____

_____

_____

_____

_____

Problem 9-3B

Part 1 Purchased January 1

	2017	2018	2019
A. Double-declining balance method			
Machinery	$588,000	$588,000	$588,000
Less: Accumulated depreciation			
Year-end book value			
Depreciation expense for the year			
B. Straight-line method			
Machinery	$588,000	$588,000	$588,000
Less: Accumulated depreciation			
Year-end book value			
Depreciation expense for the year			

Part 2 Purchased April 1

	2017	2018	2019
A. Double-declining balance method			
Machinery	$588,000	$588,000	$588,000
Less: Accumulated depreciation			
Year-end book value			
Depreciation expense for the year			
B. Straight-line method			
Machinery	$588,000	$588,000	$588,000
Less: Accumulated depreciation			
Year-end book value			
Depreciation expense for the year			

Name _____

Year	Depreciation Method		
	Straight-Line	Double-Declining-Balance	Units-of-Production
2017			
2018			
2019			
2020			
2021			
2022			
Totals			

Name _____

Year	Depreciation Method		
	Straight-Line	Double-Declining-Balance	Units-of-Production
2017			
2018			
2019			
2020			
2021			
2022			
Totals			

Calculations:

Name _____

Part 1

GENERAL JOURNAL   Page____

Date	Account Titles and Explanation	PR	Debit	Credit

Part 2

Westfair Foods

Partial Balance Sheet

December 31, 2018

Part 1

	Market Value	Percentage of Total	Apportioned Cost
Building			
Land			
Land improvements			
Truck	_____	_____	_____
Total	_____	_____	_____

GENERAL JOURNAL   Page____

Date		Account Titles and Explanation	PR	Debit	Credit

Part 2: 2017 straight-line depreciation on building:

_____
_____
_____

Part 3: 2017 double-declining-balance depreciation on land improvements:

_____
_____
_____

Name _____

Year	Depreciation		
	Straight-Line	**Units-of-Production**	**Double-Declining-Balance**
2017			
2018			
2019			
2020			
2021			
2022			
Totals			

Calculations:

	Cost Information					Depreciation		
Description	Date of Purchase	Depreciation Method	Cost	Residual	Life	Balance of Accum. Deprec. Apr. 30, 2017	Depreciation Expense for 2018	Balance of Accum. Deprec. Apr. 30, 2018
Equipment	Oct. 3/14	Straight-line	$62,400	$16,800	20 yr.			
Machinery	Oct. 28/14	Units-of-production	540,000	180,000	100,000 units			
Tools	Nov. 3/14	Double-declining-balance	64,000	15,000	5 yr.			

Calculations:

Name _____

GENERAL JOURNAL   Page____

Date	Account Titles and Explanation	PR	Debit	Credit

Calculations:

GENERAL JOURNAL   Page____

Date	Account Titles and Explanation	PR	Debit	Credit

Calculations:

Part 1: Entry to record the purchase of the new furnace:

GENERAL JOURNAL   Page____

Date	Account Titles and Explanation	PR	Debit	Credit

Calculations:

Part 2: Total depreciation expense to be recorded on the warehouse for 2017:_____

Calculations:

Windows		
Doors		
Roofing		
Siding		
Framing/Walls		
Furnace		
Misc.		
Total depreciation expense to be recorded on the warehouse for 2017 =		

Part 1   **GENERAL JOURNAL**   Page____

Date		Account Titles and Explanation	PR	Debit	Credit

Calculations:

	Book Value	Recoverable Value	Impairment Loss
Computer equipment		$ 6,250	
Land		172,500	
Machinery		65,000	
Warehouse		243,750	

Analysis component: _____

_____
_____
_____
_____
_____
_____
_____
_____
_____
_____
_____

Problem 9-14B

Part 1   GENERAL JOURNAL   Page____

Date	Account Titles and Explanation	PR	Debit	Credit

Calculations:

Part 2   **GENERAL JOURNAL**   Page_____

Date		Account Titles and Explanation	PR	Debit	Credit

Calculations:

Part 3   **GENERAL JOURNAL**   Page____

Date	Account Titles and Explanation	PR	Debit	Credit

Calculations:

Name _____

Part 1   **GENERAL JOURNAL**   Page____

Date	Account Titles and Explanation	PR	Debit	Credit

Part 2   **GENERAL JOURNAL**   Page____

Date	Account Titles and Explanation	PR	Debit	Credit

Part 3(a)   GENERAL JOURNAL   Page____

Date		Account Titles and Explanation	PR	Debit	Credit

Part 3(b)   GENERAL JOURNAL   Page____

Date		Account Titles and Explanation	PR	Debit	Credit

Part 3(c)   GENERAL JOURNAL   Page____

Date		Account Titles and Explanation	PR	Debit	Credit

Calculations:

GENERAL JOURNAL   Page____

Date	Account Titles and Explanation	PR	Debit	Credit

Calculations:

1. Depreciation expense on first December 31 of each machine's life:

GENERAL JOURNAL   Page____

Date	Account Titles and Explanation	PR	Debit	Credit

2. Purchase/exchange/disposal of each machine:

GENERAL JOURNAL   Page____

Date	Account Titles and Explanation	PR	Debit	Credit

GENERAL JOURNAL   Page_____

Date	Account Titles and Explanation	PR	Debit	Credit

Calculations:

1a.   GENERAL JOURNAL   Page____

Date	Account Titles and Explanation	PR	Debit	Credit

1b.   GENERAL JOURNAL   Page____

Date	Account Titles and Explanation	PR	Debit	Credit

Part 2

Partial Balance Sheet

Part 1   **GENERAL JOURNAL**   Page____

Date	Account Titles and Explanation	PR	Debit	Credit

Part 2   **GENERAL JOURNAL**   Page____

Date	Account Titles and Explanation	PR	Debit	Credit

Chapter 9   *Problem 9-20B   *Name* _____

1a.   **GENERAL JOURNAL**   Page____

Date	Account Titles and Explanation	PR	Debit	Credit

1b.   **GENERAL JOURNAL**   Page____

Date	Account Titles and Explanation	PR	Debit	Credit

Calculations:

Part 2

Metal Frame		
Engine	2012:	
	2013:	
	2014:	
	2015:	
	2016:	
	2017	
New Fan		
Conveyor System		
Misc. Parts	2012:	
	2013:	
	2014:	
	2015:	
	2016:	
	Total	

Current Liabilities:

_____

_____

Quick Study 10-2

1.

_____

_____

_____

_____

_____

_____

_____

2.

_____

_____

_____

_____

_____

_____

Quick Study 10-3

GENERAL JOURNAL   Page____

Date	Account Titles and Explanation	PR	Debit	Credit

Name _____

GENERAL JOURNAL

Page____

Date	Account Titles and Explanation	PR	Debit	Credit

Quick Study 10-5

GENERAL JOURNAL

Page____

Date	Account Titles and Explanation	PR	Debit	Credit

Quick Study 10-6

GENERAL JOURNAL

Page____

Date	Account Titles and Explanation	PR	Debit	Credit

Name _____

GENERAL JOURNAL   Page____

Date	Account Titles and Explanation	PR	Debit	Credit

Quick Study 10-8

GENERAL JOURNAL   Page____

Date	Account Titles and Explanation	PR	Debit	Credit

Quick Study 10-9

_____
_____
_____
_____

Quick Study 10-10

GENERAL JOURNAL   Page____

Date	Account Titles and Explanation	PR	Debit	Credit

Name _____

GENERAL JOURNAL   Page____

Date		Account Titles and Explanation	PR	Debit	Credit

Quick Study 10-12

GENERAL JOURNAL   Page____

Date		Account Titles and Explanation	PR	Debit	Credit

Quick Study 10-13

GENERAL JOURNAL   Page____

Date		Account Titles and Explanation	PR	Debit	Credit

Name _____

a. _____
_____
_____
_____

b. _____
_____
_____
_____

c. _____
_____
_____
_____

Name _____

a.		f.
b.		g.
c.		h.
d.		i.
e.		j.

Exercise 10-2

CORMORAND ELECTRONICS COMPANY
Partial Balance Sheet
December 31, 2014

Exercise 10-3

a.
GENERAL JOURNAL   Page____

Date		Account Titles and Explanation	PR	Debit	Credit

b.
GENERAL JOURNAL   Page____

Date		Account Titles and Explanation	PR	Debit	Credit

Name _____

JASPER COMPANY
Partial Balance Sheet
December 31, 2014

Analysis component:

_____
_____
_____
_____
_____
_____
_____

Exercise 10-5

1.   **GENERAL JOURNAL**   Page____

Date	Account Titles and Explanation	PR	Debit	Credit

Calculations:

2.

_____
_____
_____
_____
_____
_____
_____

Exercise 10-6

GENERAL JOURNAL Page____

Date	Account Titles and Explanation	PR	Debit	Credit

Analysis component:

_____
_____
_____
_____
_____
_____

Name _____

a.   **GENERAL JOURNAL**   Page_____

Date		Account Titles and Explanation	PR	Debit	Credit

b.   **GENERAL JOURNAL**   Page_____

Date		Account Titles and Explanation	PR	Debit	Credit

Name _____

a.   **GENERAL JOURNAL**   Page____

Date	Account Titles and Explanation	PR	Debit	Credit

b.

_____
_____
_____
_____
_____
_____
_____

Name _____

a.   Nova Scotia   GENERAL JOURNAL   Page____

Date	Account Titles and Explanation	PR	Debit	Credit

b.   British Columbia   GENERAL JOURNAL   Page____

Date	Account Titles and Explanation	PR	Debit	Credit

c.   Prince Edward Island   GENERAL JOURNAL   Page____

Date	Account Titles and Explanation	PR	Debit	Credit

d.   Alberta   GENERAL JOURNAL   Page____

Date	Account Titles and Explanation	PR	Debit	Credit

Name _____

Date	Account	Alberta/ NWT/ Nunavut/ Yukon	Manitoba	PEI	Quebec	Saskatchewan	BC	New Brunswick/ Newfoundland/ Labrador/ Ontario	Nova Scotia

Name _____

a.   **GENERAL JOURNAL**   Page____

Date	Account Titles and Explanation	PR	Debit	Credit

b.   **GENERAL JOURNAL**   Page____

Date	Account Titles and Explanation	PR	Debit	Credit

c.   **GENERAL JOURNAL**   Page____

Date	Account Titles and Explanation	PR	Debit	Credit

Fundamental Accounting Principles, 15ce, Working Papers

Name _____

1.

_____

_____

_____

_____

_____

_____

_____

_____

2.

_____

_____

3.

GENERAL JOURNAL   Page____

Date		Account Titles and Explanation	PR	Debit	Credit

Exercise 10-13

1.

_____

_____

_____

_____

_____

_____

_____

_____

2.

_____

_____

3.

_____

_____

_____

4.

GENERAL JOURNAL   Page____

Date	Account Titles and Explanation	PR	Debit	Credit

Exercise 10-14

GENERAL JOURNAL   Page____

Date	Account Titles and Explanation	PR	Debit	Credit
a.				
b.				

c.
_____

d.
_____

1.
_____
_____

2.
_____
_____

3.
_____
_____

4.
_____
_____
_____
_____
_____
_____
_____

5. Journal entries:

GENERAL JOURNAL   Page____

Date	Account Titles and Explanation	PR	Debit	Credit

Name _____

Part A   **GENERAL JOURNAL**   Page____

Date	Account Titles and Explanation	PR	Debit	Credit
1.				
2.				

Part B (Independent of Part A)

3.

	Jan. – Mar.	Apr. – June	July – Sept.	Oct. – Dec.
Income before tax				
Estimated income tax expense				
Net income				

4.

GENERAL JOURNAL   Page____

Date	Account Titles and Explanation	PR	Debit	Credit

5. _____

_____

_____

Name _____

a.

	GENERAL JOURNAL			Page____

Date	Account Titles and Explanation	PR	Debit	Credit

b.

_____

_____

c.

	GENERAL JOURNAL			Page____

Date	Account Titles and Explanation	PR	Debit	Credit

d.

	GENERAL JOURNAL			Page____

Date	Account Titles and Explanation	PR	Debit	Credit

GENERAL JOURNAL   Page____

Date	Account Titles and Explanation	PR	Debit	Credit
1a.				
1b.				
1c.				
1d.				
1e.				
1f.				

2.

Analysis component:

Balance Sheet

	December 31,			
	2014	**2015**	**2016**	**2017**

_____
_____
_____
_____
_____
_____
_____
_____
_____
_____

Problem 10-2A

1.

Maturity dates:	Ferris Inc.	Scotia Bank	National Bank
Date of the note			
Term of the note			
Maturity date			

2.   **GENERAL JOURNAL**   Page_____

Date	Account Titles and Explanation	PR	Debit	Credit

GENERAL JOURNAL   Page____

Date		Account Titles and Explanation	PR	Debit	Credit

Problem 10-3A

1. Warranty expense for November and December 2014:

_____
_____
_____
_____
_____
_____

2. Warranty expense for January 2015:

_____
_____
_____
_____
_____

3. Balance of the estimated liability as of December 31, 2014:

_____
_____
_____
_____
_____
_____

4. Balance of the estimated liability as of January 31, 2015:

_____
_____
_____
_____
_____
_____

5.

GENERAL JOURNAL   Page____

Date	Account Titles and Explanation	PR	Debit	Credit

GENERAL JOURNAL   Page____

Date	Account Titles and Explanation	PR	Debit	Credit

1. Explain how financial statements are affected due to warranties in 2014 and 2015.

_____

2. Explain how financial statements are affected in 2014 and 2015 by these subscriptions.

_____

a. Ontario   **GENERAL JOURNAL**   Page____

Date	Account Titles and Explanation	PR	Debit	Credit

b. British Columbia   GENERAL JOURNAL   Page____

Date	Account Titles and Explanation	PR	Debit	Credit

c. Alberta   **GENERAL JOURNAL**   Page____

Date	Account Titles and Explanation	PR	Debit	Credit

Name _____

EYELASH EXTENSION COMPANY
Statement of Changes in Equity
For Year Ended June 30, 2014

EYELASH EXTENSION COMPANY
Partial Balance Sheet
June 30, 2014

Calculations:

Analysis component:

_____

_____

_____

_____

_____

_____

_____

_____

_____

GENERAL JOURNAL

Page____

Date	Account Titles and Explanation	PR	Debit	Credit

Part 2

Balance Sheet

Name _____

| | December 31, | | |
2014	2015	2016	2017

Problem 10-2B

GENERAL JOURNAL

Page____

Date	Account Titles and Explanation	PR	Debit	Credit

GENERAL JOURNAL   Page____

Date	Account Titles and Explanation	PR	Debit	Credit

1. Warranty expense for November and December 2014:

_____

_____

_____

_____

_____

_____

2. Warranty expense for January 2015:

_____

_____

_____

_____

_____

_____

_____

3. Balance of the estimated liability as of December 31, 2014:

_____

_____

_____

_____

_____

_____

4. Balance of the estimated liability as of January 31, 2015:

_____

_____

_____

_____

_____

_____

_____

5.

GENERAL JOURNAL   Page____

Date	Account Titles and Explanation	PR	Debit	Credit

GENERAL JOURNAL

Date	Account Titles and Explanation	PR	Debit	Credit

Chapter 10   Problem 10-4B   *Name* _____

To: **Serge Warack, General Manager**

From: **Tara Moses, Manager, Accounting and Finance**

Subject: **Accounting treatment of contingencies and estimates in the financial statements**

_____

(blank lined page)

Name _____

a.   Nova Scotia   **GENERAL JOURNAL**   Page____

Date		Account Titles and Explanation	PR	Debit	Credit

b. Saskatchewan   **GENERAL JOURNAL**   Page____

Date	Account Titles and Explanation	PR	Debit	Credit

c. Yukon   **GENERAL JOURNAL**   Page____

Date	Account Titles and Explanation	PR	Debit	Credit

Name _____

ZEST COMPANY
Income Statement
For Year Ended November 30, 2014

ZEST COMPANY
Partial Balance Sheet
November 30, 2014

Chapter 10   Problem 10-6B (concl'd.)   *Name* _____

Calculations:

_____
_____
_____
_____
_____
_____
_____
_____
_____
_____
_____
_____
_____
_____
_____
_____
_____
_____
_____
_____
_____

Analysis component:

_____
_____
_____
_____
_____
_____
_____
_____
_____
_____
_____
_____
_____
_____
_____
_____
_____
_____
_____

Name _____

GENERAL JOURNAL

Page____

Date	Account Titles and Explanation	PR	Debit	Credit

Part 2

Balance Sheet

(a) The correct ending balance of cash and the amount of the omitted cheque:

(b) Allowance for doubtful accounts:

(c) Depreciation expense on the truck:

(d) Depreciation expense on the equipment:

e) Correct revenue and unearned revenue balances:

f) Warranty expense and estimated warranty liability:

g) Note Payable and interest expense:

h) Cost of goods sold:

Part 2   Version 1, (continued)

INTERIOR DESIGN COMPANY
Six-Column Table
December 31, 2017

Account Titles	Unadjusted Trial Balance		Adjustments		Adjusted Trial Balance	
	Dr.	Cr.	Dr.	Cr.	Dr.	Cr.
Cash						
Accounts receivable						
Allowance for doubtful accounts						
Merchandise inventory						
Delivery Truck						
Accum. depreciation, Delivery Truck						
Equipment						
Accum. depreciation, equipment						
Accounts payable						
Interest Payable						
Estimated warranty liability						
Unearned Consulting Service Revenue						
Long-term notes payable						
Ken Jones, capital						
Ken Jones, withdrawals						
Home Staging Consulting revenue						
Interest earned						
Sales						
Cost of goods sold						
Depreciation expense, delivery truck						
Depreciation expense, equipment						
Wages expense						
Interest expense						
Rent expense						
Bad debts expense						
Miscellaneous expense						
Repairs expense						
Utilities expense						
Warranty expense						
Totals						

GENERAL JOURNAL   Page_____

Date	Account Titles and Explanation	PR	Debit	Credit

Part 4   Version 1, (continued)

INTERIOR DESIGN COMPANY
Income Statement
For Year Ended December 31, 2017

INTERIOR DESIGN COMPANY
Statement of Changes in Equity
For Year Ended December 31, 2017

INTERIOR DESIGN COMPANY
Balance Sheet
December 31, 2017

Name _____

_____
_____
_____
_____
_____
_____
_____
_____
_____
_____
_____
_____
_____
_____

Quick Study 11-2

_____
_____
_____
_____

Quick Study 11-3

GENERAL JOURNAL   Page____

Date		Account Titles and Explanation	PR	Debit	Credit
mar	1	Cash		50,000	
		L.P. Capital			20,000
		B.S. Capital			30,000
		To record initial investment			
		capital investments			

Quick Study 11-4

a. $\$120,000 * 1/2 = \$60,000$

b.

GENERAL JOURNAL   Page____

Date		Account Titles and Explanation	PR	Debit	Credit
Mar	31	Income Summary		$120,000	
		B. A. Capital			60,000
		D. B. Capital			60,000
		To allocate profit and			
		close Income Summary			

c.

GENERAL JOURNAL   Page____

Date		Account Titles and Explanation	PR	Debit	Credit
Mar	31	B. A. Capital		60,000	
		D. B. Capital		60,000	
		Income Summary			$120,000
		To allocate loss + close			
		Income summary			

Quick Study 11-5

Date		Account Titles and Explanation	PR	Debit	Credit
dec	31	Income Summary		48,000	
		L.M Capital			41,500
		J.C Capital			6,500

Calculations:

	Share to Montgomery	Share to Chalmers	Total
profit			$48,000
Salary Allowances:			
Montgomery	$45,000		
Chalmers		$10,000	(55,000)
Total Salaries allocation			(7,000)
Balance allocated equally:			
Montgomery	(3,500)		
Chalmers		(3,500)	
Total allocated equally			7,000
Balance of profit			$ 0
Allocation to each partner	$41,500	$6,500	$48,000

GENERAL JOURNAL   Page____

Date		Account Titles and Explanation	PR	Debit	Credit
		J.S. Capital		56,000	
		M.Y. Capital		24,000	
		Income Summary			80,000
		To transfer the loss of			
		$80,000 from the income Summary			
		account to partners capital account.			

Calculations:

	Share to Smith	Share to Yang	Total
Loss			(80,000)
Salaries allowances			
Smith	$115,000		
Yang		$90,000	
Total salaries allocation			(205,000)
Balance of loss over allocated			($285,000)
Balance allocated 3:2			
Smith (3/5 * -$285,000)	(171,000)		
Yang (2/5 * -$285,000		(114,000)	
Total allocated 3:2			285,000
Balance of loss			$ 0
	$(56,000)	$(24,000)	($80,000)

Quick Study 11-7

GENERAL JOURNAL   Page____

Date		Account Titles and Explanation	PR	Debit	Credit
		Cash		30,000	
		Kate, Capital			30,000
		To record admission of			
		Kate by investment			
		($30,000+30,000+30,000=90,000*1/3			
		=$30,000 to kate			

Chapter 11 Quick Study 11-8   *Name* _____

GENERAL JOURNAL   Page____

Date	Account Titles and Explanation	PR	Debit	Credit
2017	Ramos, Capital		10,000	
Mar.12	Bailey, Capital		10,000	
	Kate Capital			20,000
	To record admission of			
	Kate by purchase			
	$60,000 total equity × 1/3			
	= $20,000 to Kate			

Quick Study 11-9

GENERAL JOURNAL   Page____

Date	Account Titles and Explanation	PR	Debit	Credit
June 1	Cash		30,000	
	Pollard, Capital		3,000	
	Mission, Capital		3,000	
	Bishop Capital			36,000
	To record Bishops admission			
	+ bonus; $6,000 × 1/2 $3,000			

Quick Study 11-10

GENERAL JOURNAL   Page____

Date	Account Titles and Explanation	PR	Debit	Credit
Apr 21	Cash		30,000	
	Wilson, Capital			
	Beacon, Capital			
	Metcalf, Capital			
	To record admission of			
	Wilson			

Copyright © 2016 by McGraw-Hill Education Limited. All rights reserved.

138   *Fundamental Accounting Principles*, 15ce, Working Papers

GENERAL JOURNAL   Page____

Date	Account Titles and Explanation	PR	Debit	Credit
Nov 23 2017	Stuart, Capital		35,000	
	Cash			35,000

Quick Study 11-12

GENERAL JOURNAL   Page____

Date	Account Titles and Explanation	PR	Debit	Credit
Nov. 23	Peter, Capital		22,000	
	Cash			15,000
	Oliver, Capital			5,250
	Wendell, Capital			1,750
	To record retirement			
	of Peter.			

Quick Study 11-13

GENERAL JOURNAL   Page____

Date	Account Titles and Explanation	PR	Debit	Credit
Mar. 15	Darlene, Capital		$250,000	
	Linda, Capital		25,000	
	Sue, Capital		25,000	
	Cash			300,000
	To record retirement of			
	Darlene			

Name _____

GENERAL JOURNAL   Page_____

Date	Account Titles and Explanation	PR	Debit	Credit
Apr 1	Sam Capital		87,500	
	Andrew Capital		63,000	
	Mary Capital		56,500	
	Cash			207,000

Calculations:

	Cash	Equip.	Accum. Deprec.	Sam, Capital	Andrew, Capital	Mary, Capital
Bal. prior to liquidation	$32,000	$151,000	$36,000	$65,000	$48,000	$34,000
Allocation after sales	175,000	-151,000	-36,000	22,500	15,000	22,500
Total	$207,000	0	0	87,500	63,000	56,500

Quick Study 11-15

GENERAL JOURNAL   Page_____

Date	Account Titles and Explanation	PR	Debit	Credit
April 1	Sam, Capital		53,750	
	Andrew, Capital		40,500	
	Mary, Capital		22,750	
	Cash			117,000
	To record final distribution			
	of cash to partners			

Calculations:

	Cash	Equip.	Accum. Deprec.	Sam, Capital	Andrew, Capital	Mary, Capital
Bal. prior to liquidation	$32,000	$151,000	$36,000	$65,000	$48,000	$34,000
	85,000	-151,000	-36,000	-11,500	-7,500	11,250
	117,000	0	0	53,750	40,500	22,750

Name _____

1.

_____
_____
_____
_____
_____
_____
_____
_____
_____
_____

2.

_____
_____
_____
_____
_____
_____
_____
_____
_____

3.

_____
_____
_____
_____
_____
_____
_____
_____

1.

GENERAL JOURNAL

Date	Account Titles and Explanation	PR	Debit	Credit
feb 1	Cash		80,000	
	Land		120,000	
	Building		180,000	
	Long-Term Notes payable			130,000
	Tessa Williams, Capital			80,000
	Audrey Xie, Capital			170,000
	To record initial investment			
Nov 20	T.W. Withdrawls		60,000	
	A.X. Withdrawls		45,000	
	Cash			105,000
	To record partner withdrawls			
Dec 31	Income Summary		160,000	
	T.W. capital			116,000
	A.X. capital			44,000
	To allocate profit and close			
	the income summary account			
dec 31	T.W. Capital		60,000	
	A.X. Capital		45,000	
	T.W. Withdrawls			60,000
	A.X. Withdrawls			45,000
	To close withdrawls			
	account.			

Calculations:

	Share to Williams	Share to Xie	Total
Profit			$160,000
Salary allowance:			
Williams	$90,000		
Interest Allowances:	16,000		
Williams (20% on $80,000)		34,000	
Xie (20% on $170,000)	$106,000	34,000	(140,000)
Total Salaries + interest allocation			$ 20,000
Balance			
	10,000		
		10,000	
			(20,000)
			-0-
	$116,000	$44,000	$160,000

2.

Capital account balances:

	Williams	Xie
Initial Investment	$80,000	$170,000
Withdrawls	(60,000)	(45,000)
	116,000	44,000
	$136,000	$169,000

Exercise 11-3

a.

	Share to Dallas	Share to Weiss	Total
$394,000 * ½	$197,000	$197,000	$394,000

b.

	Share to Dallas	Share to Weiss	Total
(115,000/250,000)*$394,000	$181,240		$181,240
(135,000/250,000)*$394,000		$212,760	212,760
	$181,240	$212,760	$394,000

c.

	Share to Dallas	Share to Weiss	Total
Profit			$394,000
Salary Allowances	$140,000	$70,000	
Interest Allowances:			
($115,000 * 25%)	28,750		
($135,000 * 25%)		33,750	
Total Salaries and	168,750	103,750	(272,500)

Exercise 11-4

1.

	Share to Jensen	Share to Stafford	Total
Profit			$420,000
Salary Allowances	$150,000	$75,000	
Interest Allowances			
($160,000*20%)	32,000		
($200,000*20%)		40,000	
	$182,000	$115,000	(297,000)
			123,000
Balance Profit			123,000
($123,000 * 2/5", $123,000*3/5)	73,800	49,200	(123,000)
Balance Profit			$ -0-
Shares to each Partner	255,800	164,200	420,000

2.

	Share to Jensen	Share to Stafford	Total
			(95,000)
		$75,000	
	150,000		
	32,000		
		40,000	
	182,000	115,000	(297,000)
			(392,000)
	(235,200)	(156,800)	392,000
			$0
	$(53,200)	$(41,800)	(95,000)

Name _____

1.

<table>
<tr><td colspan="6" align="center">**GENERAL JOURNAL**   Page_____</td></tr>
<tr><td>**Date**</td><td>**Account Titles and Explanation**</td><td>**PR**</td><td>**Debit**</td><td>**Credit**</td></tr>
<tr><td></td><td></td><td></td><td></td><td></td></tr>
<tr><td></td><td></td><td></td><td></td><td></td></tr>
<tr><td></td><td></td><td></td><td></td><td></td></tr>
<tr><td></td><td></td><td></td><td></td><td></td></tr>
<tr><td></td><td></td><td></td><td></td><td></td></tr>
</table>

Calculations:

	Share to Liam	Share to Katano	Total

2.

Capital account balances:	Liam	Katano

	Share to Debra	Share to Glen	Total

Calculations:

Part 1

	Share to Williams	Share to Adams	Total

Part 2   **GENERAL JOURNAL**   Page____

Date	Account Titles and Explanation	PR	Debit	Credit

Part 3

Music Works
Statement of Changes in Equity
Year Ended December 31, 2017

	Williams	Adams	Total

Music Works
Balance Sheet
December 31, 2017

Analysis component:

Name _____

a.

GENERAL JOURNAL   Page_____

Date	Account Titles and Explanation	PR	Debit	Credit
July 1	Cash		$190,000	
	Morris, Capital			$190,000
	To record admission			
	of Morris			

b.

GENERAL JOURNAL   Page_____

Date	Account Titles and Explanation	PR	Debit	Credit
July 2	Cash		230,000	
	Morris, Capital			198,000
	Hall, Capital			24,000
	Reynolds, Capital			8,000
	To record admission			
	of Morris			

c.

GENERAL JOURNAL   Page_____

Date	Account Titles and Explanation	PR	Debit	Credit
July 2	Cash		$110,000	
	Hall, Capital		48,000	
	Reynolds, Capital		16,000	
	Morris, Capital			174,000
	To record admission of			
	Morris			

Calculations: b) $(760,000 + 230,000) \times 20\% = \$198,000$

$230,000 - 198,000 = \$32,000$

$32,000 \times 75\% = \$24,000$

$32,000 \times 25\% = \$8,000$

c) $(760,000 + 110,000) \times 20\% = \$174,000$

$110,000 - 174,000 = -64,000$

$-64,000 \times 75\% = -48,000$

$-64,000 \times 25\% = -16,000$

Chapter 11   Exercise 11-9

Name _____

a.

GENERAL JOURNAL

Page____

Date		Account Titles and Explanation	PR	Debit	Credit
Sep	1	Cash		105,000	
		Liam, Capital			105,000
		To record admission of			
		new partner			
		(50,000+ 195,000+105,000)30%			
		$105,000			

b.

GENERAL JOURNAL

Page____

Date		Account Titles and Explanation	PR	Debit	Credit
Sep	1	Cash		105,000	
		Liam Capital			70,000
		Keri Capital			14,000
		Nick Capital			21,000
		(50,000+ 195,000+105,000)20%			
		=$70,000			
		105,000 - 70,000 = Bonus to old Partners			
		70,000 * 2/5 = 28,000			
		70,000 * 3/5 = 42,000			

c.

GENERAL JOURNAL

Page____

Date		Account Titles and Explanation	PR	Debit	Credit
Sep	1	Cash		105,000	
		Keri, Capital		28,000	
		Nick, Capital		42,000	
		Liam Capital			175,000
		(50,000+ 195,000 + 105,000)*50%			
		= $175,000			
		175,000 - 105,000 = Bonus to Liam			
		=70,000 70,000 * 2/5 = 28,000			
		70,000 * 3/5 = 42,000			

GENERAL JOURNAL   Page____

Date		Account Titles and Explanation	PR	Debit	Credit
Apr	30	Prince Capital		140,000	
		Queen Capital			140,000
		To record admission of			
		Queen			

Exercise 11-11

a.

GENERAL JOURNAL   Page____

Date		Account Titles and Explanation	PR	Debit	Credit
Nov	30	Tran Capital		75,000	
		Cash			75,000
		To record retirement			
		of Tran			

b.

GENERAL JOURNAL   Page____

Date		Account Titles and Explanation	PR	Debit	Credit
Nov	30	Tran Capital		75,000	
		Holt Capital		3,750	
		Barth Capital		11,250	
		Cash			90,000
		To record retirement of Tran			

c.

GENERAL JOURNAL   Page____

Date		Account Titles and Explanation	PR	Debit	Credit
Nov	30	Tran Capital		75,000	
		Holt, Capital (2/8*7500)			1,875
		Barth, Capital 6/8*7500			5,625
		To record retirement of			67,500
		Tran			

Name _____

a.   **GENERAL JOURNAL**   Page____

Date		Account Titles and Explanation	PR	Debit	Credit
Oct	14	A.M. Capital		120,000	
		Acc. depreciation		44,000	
		Car			84,000
		Cash			80,000
		To record retirement of			
		partner			

b.   **GENERAL JOURNAL**   Page____

Date		Account Titles and Explanation	PR	Debit	Credit
Oct	14	A.M. Capital		160,000	
		Acc. depreciation car		44,000	
		Car			84,000
		Cash			80,000
		B.B. Capital			20,000
		L.P Capital			20,000
		To record retirement of			
		Partner			
		(160,000 - 120,000 = 40,000 bonus to partners)			
		40,000 * 40/80 $20,000 to each partner			

c.   **GENERAL JOURNAL**   Page____

Date		Account Titles and Explanation	PR	Debit	Credit
Oct	14	A.M. Capital		60,000	
		B.B. Capital		30,000	
		L.P Capital		30,000	
		Acc. depreciation. car		40,000	
		Car			84,000
		Cash			80,000
		To record Retirement of			
		Partner			
		$120,000 - 60,000 = $60,000 bonus to A.M			
		$60,000 * 40/80 = $30,000 allocated to each partner			

Name _____

GENERAL JOURNAL

Page_____

Date	Account Titles and Explanation	PR	Debit	Credit
Jan 1	Cash		56,000	
	Accum. depreciation, equip.		89,000	
	Loss on sale of equip.		7,000	
	Equipment			152,000
	To record sale of equipment.			
1	Mark Wallace, Capital ($7,000 × 2/4)		3,500	
	Olena Dunn, Capital (7,000 × 1/4)		1,750	
	Danny lynn Capital (7,000 × 1/4)		1,750	
	Loss on sale of equipment			7,000
	To distribute loss on sale			
	of equipment to partners			
1	Accounts Payable		7,000	
	Notes Payable		12,000	
	Cash			19,000
	To pay creditors			
1	Mark Wallace Capital		27,500	
	Olena Dunn Capital		12,250	
	Danny lynn Capital		10,250	
	Cash			50,000
	To distribute remaining			
	cash to partners			
1	Cash			

Calculations:

step 1   step 3   step 2

	Cash	Equip.	Accum. Deprec. Equip.	A/P	Notes Payable	David Wallace, Capital	Olena Dunn, Capital	Danny Lin, Capital
Bal. Dec. 31/17	$13,000	$152,000	$89,000	$7,000	$12,000	$31,000	$14,000	$12,000
Sale of equipment loss of $7,000	+56,000	-152,000	-89,000			-3,500	-1,750	-1,750
Balance	$69,000	Ø	Ø	$7,000	$12,000	$27,500	$12,250	$10,250
Payement of Liabilities	-19,000			-7,000	-12,000			
	50,000	Ø	Ø	Ø	Ø	$27,500	$12,250	$10,250

Name _____

GENERAL JOURNAL

Page____

Date	Account Titles and Explanation	PR	Debit	Credit
	Martha Wheaton Capital		380,000	
	Sam Smith Capital		376,000	
	Cash			756,000
	To distribute remaining			
	cash to partners			

Calculations:

128,000   2.1.1

	Cash	Building	Accum. Deprec. Bldg.	Land	A/P	Martha Wheaton, Capital	Bess Chen, Capital	Sam Smith, Capital
Bal. Dec. 31/17	$184,000	$824,000	$480,000	$208,000	$128,000	$316,000	$(52,000)	$344,000
Selling of Land & Building	680,000	-824,000	-480,000	-208,000		64,000	32,000	32,000
Balance after sale	864,000	Ø	Ø	Ø	$128,000	380,000	(20,000)	376,000
Payment of liabilities	128,000				-128,000			
total cash	$736,000	Ø	Ø	Ø	Ø	380,000	(20,000)	376,000

Additional calculations:

$680,000 - ($824,000 - $480,000 + $208,000) = $128,000 gain

$128,000 * 2/4 = $64,000 to Wheaton

$128,000 * 1/4 = $32,000 to Chen + Smith

Name _____

GENERAL JOURNAL

Page_____

Date		Account Titles and Explanation	PR	Debit	Credit

Calculations:

	Cash	Building	Accum. Deprec. Bldg.	Land	A/P	Martha Wheaton, Capital	Bess Chen, Capital	Sam Smith, Capital
Bal. Dec. 31/17	$184,000	$824,000	$480,000	$208,000	$128,000	$316,000	$(52,000)	$344,000

Exercise 11-16

1.

	Lea	Eva	Sophia	Total

2.

GENERAL JOURNAL Page____

Date	Account Titles and Explanation	PR	Debit	Credit
3. a.				
b.				

Fundamental Accounting Principles, 15ce, Working Papers

Name _____

a. <p style="text-align:center">**GENERAL JOURNAL**</p>   Page____

Date	Account Titles and Explanation	PR	Debit	Credit

b. <p style="text-align:center">**GENERAL JOURNAL**</p>   Page____

Date	Account Titles and Explanation	PR	Debit	Credit

c. <p style="text-align:center">**GENERAL JOURNAL**</p>   Page____

Date	Account Titles and Explanation	PR	Debit	Credit

Name _____

Calculations:

	Share to Jenkins	Share to Willis	Share to Trent	Total

Problem 11-2A

Plan a.

Year	Calculations	Share to Phillip	Share to Case	Total
1				
2				
3				

Fundamental Accounting Principles, 15ce, Working Papers

Plan b.

Year	Calculations	Share to Phillip	Share to Case	Total
1				
2				
3				

Plan c.

Year	Calculations	Share to Phillip	Share to Case	Total
1				

Plan c. (cont'd.)

Year	Calculations	Share to Phillip	Share to Case	Total
2				
3				

Plan d.

Year	Calculations	Share to Phillip	Share to Case	Total
1				
2				

Plan d. (concl'd.)

Year	Calculations	Share to Phillip	Share to Case	Total
3				

Chapter 11   Problem 11-3A   Name _____

Part 1

a.

	Share to Conway	Share to Chan	Share to Scott	Total

b.

	Share to Conway	Share to Chan	Share to Scott	Total

Chapter 11   Problem 11-3A (cont'd.)   Name _____

c.

	Share to Conway	Share to Chan	Share to Scott	Total

CCS Consulting
Statement of Changes in Equity
For Year Ended December 31, 2017

	Conway	Chan	Scott	Total

Part 3

GENERAL JOURNAL   Page____

Date		Account Titles and Explanation	PR	Debit	Credit

GENERAL JOURNAL   Page____

Date		Account Titles and Explanation	PR	Debit	Credit

Name _____

a.

GENERAL JOURNAL

Page____

Date	Account Titles and Explanation	PR	Debit	Credit

b.

GENERAL JOURNAL

Page____

Date	Account Titles and Explanation	PR	Debit	Credit

c.   **GENERAL JOURNAL**   Page____

Date	Account Titles and Explanation	PR	Debit	Credit

Problem 11-5A Part 1

a.   **GENERAL JOURNAL**   Page____

Date	Account Titles and Explanation	PR	Debit	Credit

b.   **GENERAL JOURNAL**   Page____

Date	Account Titles and Explanation	PR	Debit	Credit

c.   **GENERAL JOURNAL**   Page____

Date		Account Titles and Explanation	PR	Debit	Credit

Supporting calculations:

	Share to Bow	Share to Amri	Total

d.   **GENERAL JOURNAL**   Page____

Date		Account Titles and Explanation	PR	Debit	Credit

2.

Capital account balances:		Bow	Amri

Problem 11-6A

a.   **GENERAL JOURNAL**   Page____

Date		Account Titles and Explanation	PR	Debit	Credit

b.   **GENERAL JOURNAL**   Page____

Date		Account Titles and Explanation	PR	Debit	Credit

c.   **GENERAL JOURNAL**   Page____

Date		Account Titles and Explanation	PR	Debit	Credit

d.   **GENERAL JOURNAL**   Page____

Date		Account Titles and Explanation	PR	Debit	Credit

e.   **GENERAL JOURNAL**   Page____

Date		Account Titles and Explanation	PR	Debit	Credit

Name _____

Part 1

a.

	Cash	Machinery	Accum. Deprec., Machinery	Accounts Payable	Jim Lui, Capital	Kent Montavo, Capital	Dave Johnson, Capital
Bal. June 30/17	$68,750	$588,750	$137,500	$130,375	$76,250	$200,875	$112,500

Calculations:

b.

	Cash	Machinery	Accum. Deprec., Machinery	Accounts Payable	Jim Lui, Capital	Kent Montavo, Capital	Dave Johnson, Capital
Bal. June 30/17	$68,750	$588,750	$137,500	$130,375	$76,250	$200,875	$112,500

Calculations:

c.

	Cash	Machinery	Accum. Deprec., Machinery	Accounts Payable	Jim Lui, Capital	Kent Montavo, Capital	Dave Johnson, Capital
Bal. June 30/17	$68,750	$588,750	$137,500	$130,375	$76,250	$200,875	$112,500

Calculations:

d.

	Cash	Machinery	Accum. Deprec., Machinery	Accounts Payable	Jim Lui, Capital	Kent Montavo, Capital	Dave Johnson, Capital
Bal. June 30/17	$68,750	$588,750	$137,500	$130,375	$76,250	$200,875	$112,500

Calculations:

Part 2

GENERAL JOURNAL   Page____

Date		Account Titles and Explanation	PR	Debit	Credit

Chapter 11   Problem 11-8A   *Name* _____

a.   **GENERAL JOURNAL**   Page____

Date	Account Titles and Explanation	PR	Debit	Credit
b.				

GENERAL JOURNAL   Page____

Date	Account Titles and Explanation	PR	Debit	Credit

Problem 11-1B

a.   ## GENERAL JOURNAL   Page____

Date	Account Titles and Explanation	PR	Debit	Credit

b.   ## GENERAL JOURNAL   Page____

Date	Account Titles and Explanation	PR	Debit	Credit

GENERAL JOURNAL   Page____

Date		Account Titles and Explanation	PR	Debit	Credit

Calculations:

	Share to Phung	Share to Moier	Share to Lister	Total

Plan a.

Year	Calculations	Share to Bosch	Share to Gilbert	Total
1				
2				
3				

Plan b.

Year	Calculations	Share to Bosch	Share to Gilbert	Total
1				
2				
3				

Fundamental Accounting Principles, 15ce, Working Papers

Plan c.

Year	Calculations	Share to Bosch	Share to Gilbert	Total
1				

Plan c.

Year	Calculations	Share to Bosch	Share to Gilbert	Total
2				

Plan c. (cont'd.)

Year	Calculations	Share to Bosch	Share to Gilbert	Total
3				

Plan d.

Year	Calculations	Share to Bosch	Share to Gilbert	Total
1				

Plan d. (concl'd.)

Year	Calculations	Share to Bosch	Share to Gilbert	Total
2				

Year	Calculations	Share to Bosch	Share to Gilbert	Total
3				

Chapter 11   Problem 11-3B   *Name* _____

Part 1
a.

	Share to Jobs	Share to Alford	Share to Norris	Total

b.

	Share to Jobs	Share to Alford	Share to Norris	Total

c.

	Share to Jobs	Share to Alford	Share to Norris	Total

Fundamental Accounting Principles, 15ce, Working Papers

Part 2

JAN Partnership
Statement of Changes in Equity
For Year Ended December 31, 2017

	Jobs	Alford	Norris	Total

Part 3

GENERAL JOURNAL   Page____

Date	Account Titles and Explanation	PR	Debit	Credit

Name _____

a.   **GENERAL JOURNAL**   Page____

Date		Account Titles and Explanation	PR	Debit	Credit

b.   **GENERAL JOURNAL**   Page____

Date		Account Titles and Explanation	PR	Debit	Credit

c.   **GENERAL JOURNAL**   Page____

Date		Account Titles and Explanation	PR	Debit	Credit

Name _____

1 a.   **GENERAL JOURNAL**   Page____

Date	Account Titles and Explanation	PR	Debit	Credit

b.   **GENERAL JOURNAL**   Page____

Date	Account Titles and Explanation	PR	Debit	Credit

Supporting calculations:

	Share to Harris	Share to Davis	Share to Tallis	Total

Chapter 11   Problem 11-5B (concl'd.)   *Name* _____

c.   **GENERAL JOURNAL**   Page____

Date	Account Titles and Explanation	PR	Debit	Credit

2.

Capital account balances:

	Harris	Davis	Tallis

Problem 11-6B

a.   **GENERAL JOURNAL**   Page____

Date	Account Titles and Explanation	PR	Debit	Credit

b.   **GENERAL JOURNAL**   Page____

Date	Account Titles and Explanation	PR	Debit	Credit

GENERAL JOURNAL   Page____

Date	Account Titles and Explanation	PR	Debit	Credit

GENERAL JOURNAL   Page____

Date	Account Titles and Explanation	PR	Debit	Credit

GENERAL JOURNAL   Page____

Date	Account Titles and Explanation	PR	Debit	Credit

1a.

	Cash	Equip.	Accum. Deprec., Equip.	A/P	Ernie Poppy, Capital	Lynn Sweetbean, Capital	Ned Olive, Capital
Bal. Oct. 15/17	$9,450	$206,920	$40,600	$39,690	$63,840	$42,000	$30,240

Calculations:

1b.

	Cash	Equip.	Accum. Deprec., Equip.	A/P	Ernie Poppy, Capital	Lynn Sweetbean, Capital	Ned Olive, Capital
Bal. Oct. 15/17	$9,450	$206,920	$40,600	$39,690	$63,840	$42,000	$30,240

Calculations:

1c.

	Cash	Equip.	Accum. Deprec., Equip.	A/P	Ernie Poppy, Capital	Lynn Sweetbean, Capital	Ned Olive, Capital
Bal. Oct. 15/17	$9,450	$206,920	$40,600	$39,690	$63,840	$42,000	$30,240

Calculations:

1d.

	Cash	Equip.	Accum. Deprec., Equip.	A/P	Ernie Poppy, Capital	Lynn Sweetbean, Capital	Ned Olive, Capital
Bal. Oct. 15/17	$9,450	$206,920	$40,600	$39,690	$63,840	$42,000	$30,240

Calculations:

Part 2   GENERAL JOURNAL   Page____

Date	Account Titles and Explanation	PR	Debit	Credit

Problem 11-8B

a.   GENERAL JOURNAL   Page____

Date	Account Titles and Explanation	PR	Debit	Credit

GENERAL JOURNAL   Page____

Date	Account Titles and Explanation	PR	Debit	Credit

b.

GENERAL JOURNAL   Page____

Date	Account Titles and Explanation	PR	Debit	Credit

GENERAL JOURNAL   Page____

Date	Account Titles and Explanation	PR	Debit	Credit

Name _____

_____

_____

Quick Study 12-2

MOGUL LTD.		
Income Statement		
For Year Ended October 31, 2017		

Quick Study 12-3

_____	Cash	_____	Preferred shares
_____	Common shares	_____	Retained earnings
_____	Common dividend payable	_____	Preferred dividend payable
_____	Deficit	_____	Preferred shares, $5 noncumulative

FORM OF BUSINESS ORGANIZATION

Sole Proprietorship	Corporation

Cash ....
   Ian Smith, Capital ....

Cash ....
   Revenues ....

Expenses ....
   Cash ....

Ian Smith, Withdrawals ....
   Cash ....

Revenues ....
   Income Summary ....

Income Summary ....
   Expenses ....

Income Summary ....
   Ian Smith, Capital ....

Ian Smith, Capital ....
   Ian Smith, Withdrawals ....

Cash ....
   Common Shares ....

Cash ....
   Revenues ....

Expenses ....
   Cash ....

Cash Dividends ....
   Cash ....

Revenues ....
   Income Summary ....

Income Summary ....
   Expenses ....

Income Summary ....
   Retained Earnings ....

Retained Earnings ....
   Cash Dividends ....

Vision HR Consulting
Partial Balance Sheet
December 31, 2017

Equity
   Ian Smith, capital

   Total equity

Vision HR Consulting Inc.
Partial Balance Sheet
December 31, 2017

Equity
   Common shares
   Retained earnings
   Total equity

Quick Study 12-5

_____   *OR*   _____   **Retained Earnings**
_____

Name _____

1. _____
2. _____
3. _____

Quick Study 12-7

Fisher Inc			
Statement of Changes in Equity			
For Year Ended December 21, 2018			

Quick Study 12-8

GENERAL JOURNAL   Page_____

Date	Account Titles and Explanation	PR	Debit	Credit

Average issue price per common share: _____
_____
_____

Quick Study 12-9

a. _____
b. _____
c. _____

Name _____

a.

GENERAL JOURNAL   Page_____

Date	Account Titles and Explanation	PR	Debit	Credit

b. _____

_____

Quick Study 12-11

GENERAL JOURNAL   Page_____

Date	Account Titles and Explanation	PR	Debit	Credit

a.

b.

Quick Study 12-13

a.

b.

c.

d.

e.

f.

a.   **GENERAL JOURNAL**   Page____

Date	Account Titles and Explanation	PR	Debit	Credit

b.

PETER PUCK INC.

Statement of Changes in Equity

For Year Ended May 31, 2017

a.

GENERAL JOURNAL   Page____

Date	Account Titles and Explanation	PR	Debit	Credit

b.

MORRIS INC.
Statement of Changes in Equity
For Year Ended November 30, 2017

a.   **GENERAL JOURNAL**   Page____

Date	Account Titles and Explanation	PR	Debit	Credit

b.

VELOR LTD.

Statement of Changes in Equity

For Year Ended August 31, 2017

Quick Study 12-17

_____

_____

_____

_____

_____

1.

GENERAL JOURNAL   Page____

Date	Account Titles and Explanation	PR	Debit	Credit

2.

Date	Account Titles and Explanation	PR	Debit	Credit

GENERAL JOURNAL

Page____

Date	Account Titles and Explanation	PR	Debit	Credit

Exercise 12-2

GENERAL JOURNAL

Page____

Date	Account Titles and Explanation	PR	Debit	Credit

a.

GENERAL JOURNAL   Page____

Date		Account Titles and Explanation	PR	Debit	Credit

b.

FIERRA SCEPTRE INC.
Equity Section of the Balance Sheet
December 31, 2017

c. _____

_____

_____

Calculations:

Exercise 12-4

GENERAL JOURNAL   Page____

Date	Account Titles and Explanation	PR	Debit	Credit

GENERAL JOURNAL   Page____

Date	Account Titles and Explanation	PR	Debit	Credit

Name _____

a.   **GENERAL JOURNAL**   Page____

Date	Account Titles and Explanation	PR	Debit	Credit

b.

WESTBY CORP.

Equity Section of the Balance Sheet

January 31, 2017

c. _____
_____
_____

Calculations:

Exercise 12-7

1.

_____
_____
_____
_____
_____
_____
_____
_____
_____

2.

	OR	**Retained Earnings**

3.

ZOOMZOOM INC.					
Statement of Changes in Equity					
For Year Ended December 31, 2017					

WHITE PEAR INC.
Equity Section of the Balance Sheet
December 31, 2017

Calculations:

Exercise 12-9

1.

2.

3.

4.

5.

6.

7.

8.

Name _____

	Preferred	Common
2017:		
2018:		
2019:		
2020:		
Total for four years:		

	Preferred	**Common**
2017:		

_____

_____

_____

_____

2018: _____

_____

_____

_____

_____

2019: _____

_____

_____

_____

_____

2020: _____

_____

_____

_____

_____

_____

Total for four years: _____

Exercise 12-12

1. _____	4. _____
2. _____	5. _____
3. _____	6. _____

Exercise 12-13

1. _____

2. _____

_____

GENERAL JOURNAL

Date	Account Titles and Explanation	PR	Debit	Credit

_____   *OR*   Retained Earnings

SPICER INC.
Balance Sheet
December 31, 2017

Name _____

1.   **GENERAL JOURNAL**   Page____

Date	Account Titles and Explanation	PR	Debit	Credit

2.   **DELICIOUS ALTERNATIVE DESSERTS INC.**

Equity Section of the Balance Sheet

December 31, 2017

3. _____

_____

4. _____

_____

Calculations:

Exercise 12-17

Part A   **GENERAL JOURNAL**   Page____

Date	Account Titles and Explanation	PR	Debit	Credit

Part A   **GENERAL JOURNAL**   Page____

Date	Account Titles and Explanation	PR	Debit	Credit

Part B

EARTH STAR DIAMONDS INC.

Balance Sheet

October 31, 2017

Name _____

_____
_____
_____
_____
_____
_____
_____
_____
_____

Name   _____

SASSY PHARMACEUTICALS INC.
Balance Sheet
March 31, 2017

Analysis component:

_____
_____
_____
_____
_____
_____
_____
_____
_____
_____
_____

Problem 12-2A

_____
_____
_____
_____
_____
_____
_____
_____
_____
_____
_____
_____
_____

Name _____

GENERAL JOURNAL

Page____

Date		Account Titles and Explanation	PR	Debit	Credit

_____
_____
_____
_____
_____
_____
_____
_____
_____

Analysis component:

_____
_____
_____
_____
_____
_____
_____
_____
_____
_____
_____
_____
_____
_____
_____
_____
_____
_____

Name _____

1. _____

2. _____
   _____

3. _____

4. _____

5. _____

6a. _____

6b. _____

7a. _____

7b. _____

8. _____

9. _____
   _____

10. _____
    _____
    _____

Chapter 12   Problem 12-5A   *Name* _____

Part A – Non-cumulative

1.

Year	Preferred Dividends	Common Dividends	Total Dividends
2015			
2016			
2017			
Totals			

2. _____
_____
_____

Part B - Cumulatives

1.

Year	Preferred Dividends	Common Dividends	Total Dividends
2015			
2016			
2017			
Totals			

2. _____
_____
_____

Analysis component: _____
_____
_____
_____
_____
_____
_____
_____

Part 1. Journal entries:

GENERAL JOURNAL   Page____

Date	Account Titles and Explanation	PR	Debit	Credit

Part 2

UMI SUSTAINABLE SEAFOOD INC.
Statement of Changes in Equity
For Year Ended December 31, 2018

Part 3

UMI SUSTAINABLE SEAFOOD INC.
Equity Section of the Balance Sheet
December 31, 2018

Calculations:

Analysis component:

Name _____

GENERAL JOURNAL

Page____

Date	Account Titles and Explanation	PR	Debit	Credit

GENERAL JOURNAL   Page____

Date	Account Titles and Explanation	PR	Debit	Credit

Part 2

HAMMOND MANUFACTURING INC.
Statement of Changes in Equity
For Year Ended December 31, 2019

Part 3

HAMMOND MANUFACTURING INC.
Equity Section of the Balance Sheet
December 31, 2019

Calculations:

Analysis component:

	2015	2016	2017
Net Assets = A – L or E			
Trend (F or U)			

Name _____

Part 1   **GENERAL JOURNAL**   Page____

Date	Account Titles and Explanation	PR	Debit	Credit

GENERAL JOURNAL   Page____

Date	Account Titles and Explanation	PR	Debit	Credit

Part 2

TACTEX CONTROLS INC.
Statement of Changes in Equity
For Year Ended December 31, 2018

Part 3

TAXTEC CONTROLS INC.
Equity Section of the Balance Sheet
December 31, 2018

Calculations:

_____

_____

_____

_____

_____

_____

_____

_____

_____

_____

_____

_____

Name _____

MALTA INDUSTRIES INC.
Balance Sheet
October 31, 2017

Chapter 12   Problem 12-2B   *Name* _____

Calculations

_____
_____
_____
_____
_____
_____
_____
_____
_____
_____
_____
_____
_____
_____

Problem 12-3B

GENERAL JOURNAL   Page____

Date	Account Titles and Explanation	PR	Debit	Credit

Analysis component:

1. _____

2. _____

3. _____

4. _____

5. _____

6. _____

7. _____

Problem 12-5B

1.

Year	Dividends Declared and Paid	Preferred Dividends	Common Dividends
2016			
2017			
2018			
2019			

2.

Year	Dividends Declared and Paid	Preferred Dividends	Common Dividends
2016			
2017			
2018			
2019			

Problem 12-6B

Part 1. Journal entries:

GENERAL JOURNAL

Page____

Date	Account Titles and Explanation	PR	Debit	Credit

GENERAL JOURNAL   Page____

Date	Account Titles and Explanation	PR	Debit	Credit

Part 2

GENERAL JOURNAL   Page____

QUICKSTREAM INC.
Statement of Changes in Equity
For Year Ended December 31, 2018

Part 3

QUICKSTREAM INC.

Equity Section of the Balance Sheet

December 31, 2018

Calculations: _____

_____

_____

_____

_____

_____

_____

_____

Analysis component: _____

_____

_____

_____

_____

_____

_____

Problem 12-7B

Part 1

GENERAL JOURNAL   Page_____

Date	Account Titles and Explanation	PR	Debit	Credit

GENERAL JOURNAL

Date	Account Titles and Explanation	PR	Debit	Credit

Part 2

LABTECH PHARMACY INC.
Statement of Changes in Equity
For Year Ended December 31, 2017

Part 3

LABTECH PHARMACY INC.
Equity Section of the Balance Sheet
December 31, 2017

Calculations:

Analysis component:

	2015	2016	2017
Net Assets = A – L or E			
Trend (F or U)			

Name _____

Part 1   **GENERAL JOURNAL**   Page____

Date	Account Titles and Explanation	PR	Debit	Credit

GENERAL JOURNAL   Page____

Date	Account Titles and Explanation	PR	Debit	Credit

Part 2

PACE OIL & GAS CORP.

Statement of Changes in Equity

For Year Ended December 31, 2017

Part 3

PACE OIL & GAS CORP

Equity Section of the Balance Sheet

December 31, 2017

Calculations:

Name _____

Jamestown Corp.
Equity Section of the Balance Sheet
April 1, 2017

Quick Study 13-2

Vector Gaming Ltd.
Equity Section of the Balance Sheet

	Dec. 31, 2017 Before Share Split	Jan. 2, 2018 After Share Split

Quick Study 13-3

GENERAL JOURNAL   Page____

Date	Account Titles and Explanation	PR	Debit	Credit

Name _____

GENERAL JOURNAL

Page____

Date		Account Titles and Explanation	PR	Debit	Credit

Quick Study 13-5

_____
_____
_____
_____
_____
_____
_____
_____

Quick Study 13-6

_____
_____
_____
_____
_____
_____
_____
_____
_____

Chapter 13   Quick Study 13-7   *Name* _____

Time Period	Outstanding Shares	Fraction of Year Outstanding	Weighted Average

Quick Study 13-8

Time Period	Outstanding Shares	Effect of Share Dividend	Fraction of Year Outstanding	Weighted Average

Quick Study 13-9

Time Period	Outstanding Shares	Effect of Share Split	Fraction of Year Outstanding	Weighted Average

Quick Study 13-10

Time Period	Outstanding Shares	Fraction of Year Outstanding	Weighted Average

Quick Study 13-11

a. Gain on sale of Division E ..... _____
b. Operating expenses .... _____
c. Loss on sale of equipment .... _____
d. Interest income .... _____
e. Depreciation expense .... _____
f. Earnings per share .... _____

g. Cost of goods sold .... _____
h. Loss from operating Division E ... _____
i. Income tax expense .... _____
j. Gain on sale of warehouse .... _____
k. Interest expense .... _____

Copyright © 2016 by McGraw-Hill Education Limited. All rights reserved.off

242   *Fundamental Accounting Principles*, 15ce, Working Papersoff

a.
_____
_____
_____
_____
_____
_____

b.
_____
_____
_____
_____
_____
_____

Quick Study 13-13

GENERAL JOURNAL   Page____

Date	Account Titles and Explanation	PR	Debit	Credit

Part 1   **GENERAL JOURNAL**   Page____

Date		Account Titles and Explanation	PR	Debit	Credit

Part 2

Arcus Development Inc.
Equity Section of the Balance Sheet
January 31, 2017

Calculations:

Analysis component:

_____
_____
_____
_____
_____
_____
_____

Parts 1 and 2   **GENERAL JOURNAL**   Page____

Date	Account Titles and Explanation	PR	Debit	Credit

Part 3

Pacifica Papers Inc.
Equity Section of the Balance Sheet
December 31, 2017

Calculations:

Part 1   **GENERAL JOURNAL**   Page____

Date	Account Titles and Explanation	PR	Debit	Credit

Part 2

Bandara Gold Inc.
Equity Section of the Balance Sheet
November 30, 2017

Calculations:

Analysis component:

_____

_____

_____

_____

_____

_____

_____

Name _____

Part 1

VisionTech Inc.

Statement of Changes in Equity

For Year Ended December 31, 2017

Part 2

VisionTech Inc.

Equity Section of the Balance Sheet

December 31, 2017

Calculations:

Name

Carfind Inc.
Equity Section of the Balance Sheet
December 31, 2017

Calculations:

Analysis component:

GENERAL JOURNAL

Page____

Date	Account Titles and Explanation	PR	Debit	Credit

Exercise 13-7   Part 1

GENERAL JOURNAL

Page____

Date	Account Titles and Explanation	PR	Debit	Credit

GENERAL JOURNAL   Page____

Date		Account Titles and Explanation	PR	Debit	Credit

Part 2

The Data Group Inc.
Equity Section of the Balance Sheet
December 31, 2017

Calculations:

Analysis component: _____

_____

_____

_____

_____

Name _____

a.

	GENERAL JOURNAL			Page____

Date	Account Titles and Explanation	PR	Debit	Credit

b.

Mady Entertainment Inc.
Equity Section of the Balance Sheet
December 31, 2017

Calculations:

_____
_____
_____
_____
_____
_____
_____
_____
_____
_____
_____
_____
_____
_____
_____
_____
_____
_____
_____
_____
_____
_____
_____
_____

Exercise 13-9

_____
_____
_____
_____
_____
_____
_____
_____
_____
_____

Name _____

_____
_____
_____
_____
_____
_____
_____
_____

Calculations:

Time Period	Outstanding Shares	Effect of Share Dividend	Fraction of Year Outstanding	Weighted Average*

Round to nearest whole share

Exercise 13-11

_____
_____
_____
_____
_____
_____
_____

Calculations:

Time Period	Outstanding Shares	Effect of Share Dividend	Fraction of Year Outstanding	Weighted Average*

Round to nearest whole share

Analysis component:

_____
_____
_____
_____
_____
_____

Name _____

a. _____
_____
_____
_____
_____

b.

Time Period	Outstanding Shares	Effect of Share Dividend	Fraction of Year Outstanding	Weighted Average*

Round to nearest whole share

c. _____
_____
_____
_____
_____
_____
_____
_____

Analysis component:
_____
_____
_____
_____
_____
_____
_____
_____

Fundamental Accounting Principles, 15ce, Working Papers

a. _____
_____
_____
_____
_____
_____

b.

Time Period	Outstanding Shares	Effect of Share Split	Fraction of Year Outstanding	Weighted Average*

Round to nearest whole share

c. _____
_____
_____
_____
_____
_____
_____
_____

Analysis component:

_____
_____
_____
_____
_____
_____
_____
_____

Name

Future Products Corp.
Income Statement
For Year Ended December 31, 2017

Fundamental Accounting Principles, 15ce, Working Papers

Name _____

a.
_____
_____
_____
_____
_____

b.
_____
_____
_____
_____
_____

c.
_____
_____
_____
_____

Exercise 13-16

1.

2.
_____

3.
_____

4.
_____

5.
_____

6.
_____

7.
_____

8.
_____

GlenTel Inc.		
Income Statement		
For Year Ended December 31, 2017		

Name   _____

a.

Ice Industries Inc.
Statement of Changes in Equity
For Year Ended December 31, 2017

Notes to Financial Statements:

_____
_____
_____
_____
_____
_____
_____

b.

_____
_____
_____

Exercise 13-19

_____
_____
_____
_____
_____
_____
_____
_____
_____
_____

Name _____

Infinity Minerals Corp.
Statement of Changes in Equity
For Year Ended December 31, 2017

Chapter 13   Problem 13-1A   *Name* _____

Part 1

	(c) 2018	(b) 2017	(a) 2016

Part 2

a. 2016 weighted-average shares:

Time Period	Outstanding Shares	Effect of Share Dividend	Fraction of Year Outstanding	Weighted Average*

b. 2017 weighted-average shares:

Time Period	Outstanding Shares	Fraction of Year Outstanding	Weighted Average*

c. 2018 weighted-average shares:

Time Period	Outstanding Shares	Effect of Share Split	Fraction of Year Outstanding	Weighted Average*

*Round to the nearest whole share

Part 3: Earnings per share

	(c) **2018**	(b) **2017**	(a) **2016**

Analysis component:

_____
_____
_____
_____
_____
_____
_____

Problem 13-2A

1. _____
_____
_____
_____
_____
_____
_____
_____
_____
_____
_____
_____
_____

2. _____
_____
_____
_____
_____
_____
_____
_____
_____

Name   _____

Part 1   Journal entries:

GENERAL JOURNAL   Page____

Date	Account Titles and Explanation	PR	Debit	Credit

GENERAL JOURNAL   Page____

Date	Account Titles and Explanation	PR	Debit	Credit

Part 2

Zen Aerospace Corporation
Statement of Changes in Equity
For Year Ended December 31, 2017

Name _____

Part 1: Effect of income taxes (losses in parentheses)

Measure	Pre-Tax	30% Tax Effect	After-Tax

Part 2: Multi-step income statement

Telecom Corp.
Income Statement
Year Ended December 31, 2017

Weatherford International Inc.

Income Statement

For Year Ended December 31, 2017

Part 1

Kaye Biotech Inc.				
Statement of Changes in Equity				
For Year Ended December 31, 2017				

Calculations:

Name _____

Part 1

	Jan. 5	Apr. 5	July 5	Oct. 5

Part 2
Profit:

Chapter 13   Problem 13-1B   *Name* _____

Part 1

	(c) 2018	(b) 2017	(a) 2016

_____
_____
_____
_____
_____
_____
_____
_____

Part 2

a. 2016 weighted-average shares:

Time Period	Outstanding Shares	Effect of Share Dividend	Fraction of Year Outstanding	Weighted Average*

b. 2017 weighted-average shares:

Time Period	Outstanding Shares	Fraction of Year Outstanding	Weighted Average*

c. 2018 weighted-average shares:

Time Period	Outstanding Shares	Effect of Share Split	Fraction of Year Outstanding	Weighted Average*

Round to the nearest whole share

Part 3: Earnings per share

	(c) 2018	(b) 2017	(a) 2016

Problem 13-2B

1. _____

_____

_____

_____

_____

_____

_____

_____

_____

_____

_____

2. _____

_____

_____

_____

_____

_____

_____

_____

Name _____

Part 1   Journal entries:

GENERAL JOURNAL   Page____

Date	Account Titles and Explanation	PR	Debit	Credit

GENERAL JOURNAL

Page____

Date	Account Titles and Explanation	PR	Debit	Credit

Part 2

Kalimantan Corp.
Statement of Changes in Equity
For Year Ended December 31, 2017

Part 1: Effect of income taxes (losses in parentheses)

Measure	Pre-Tax	25% Tax Effect	After-Tax

Part 2: Multi-step income statement

Decoma International Corp.
Income Statement
Year Ended December 31, 2017

Online Hearing Inc.
Income Statement
For Year Ended December 31, 2017

Part 1

Venir Exchange Corp.
Statement of Changes in Equity
For Year Ended December 31, 2017

Calculations:

Name _____

Part 1

	Feb. 15	May 15	Aug. 15	Nov. 15

Part 2
Profit:

a.

b.

c.

d.

Quick Study 14-2

a.

b.

Quick Study 14-3

serial bonds		bearer bonds
convertible bonds		secured bonds
registered bonds		debentures
		bond indenture

Quick Study 14-4

GENERAL JOURNAL   Page____

Date	Account Titles and Explanation	PR	Debit	Credit
a.				
b.				
c.				

GENERAL JOURNAL   Page____

Date	Account Titles and Explanation	PR	Debit	Credit

Quick Study 14-6

	a.	b.	c.
PV of face amount			
PV of interest annuity			
Total issue price			

Calculations:

Quick Study 14-7

	a.	b.	c.
PV of face amount			
PV of interest annuity			
Total issue price			

Calculations:

Name _____

GENERAL JOURNAL   Page____

Date	Account Titles and Explanation	PR	Debit	Credit

Quick Study 14-9

a.

_____
_____
_____
_____
_____

b.

_____
_____

Quick Study 14-10

GENERAL JOURNAL   Page____

Date	Account Titles and Explanation	PR	Debit	Credit

Name _____

a.

_____
_____
_____
_____
_____

b.

_____
_____

Quick Study 14-12

GENERAL JOURNAL   Page____

Date	Account Titles and Explanation	PR	Debit	Credit

Name _____

GENERAL JOURNAL   Page____

Date		Account Titles and Explanation	PR	Debit	Credit

Quick Study 14-14

GENERAL JOURNAL   Page____

Date		Account Titles and Explanation	PR	Debit	Credit

GENERAL JOURNAL   Page____

Date	Account Titles and Explanation	PR	Debit	Credit

Quick Study 14-16

	2017	**2018**	**2019**
Beginning balance			
Interest rate			
Interest expense			
Ending balance			

Quick Study 14-17

a. _____

b. _____

c. _____

Quick Study 14-18

_____

_____

_____

Name _____

Part a

	Fab Form Industries		Recycle Resources		Outdoor Adventure Company	
	2017	**2016**	**2017**	**2016**	**2017**	**2016**
Total Debt (A)						
Total Equity (B)						

Part b

_____

_____

_____

_____

_____

_____

_____

Name _____

a. _____

_____

b.   **GENERAL JOURNAL**   Page____

Date	Account Titles and Explanation	PR	Debit	Credit

Exercise 14-2

a. _____

_____

b.   **GENERAL JOURNAL**   Page____

Date	Account Titles and Explanation	PR	Debit	Credit

Name _____

a.   **GENERAL JOURNAL**   Page____

Date	Account Titles and Explanation	PR	Debit	Credit

b.   **GENERAL JOURNAL**   Page____

Date	Account Titles and Explanation	PR	Debit	Credit

c.   **GENERAL JOURNAL**   Page____

Date	Account Titles and Explanation	PR	Debit	Credit

d.   **GENERAL JOURNAL**   Page____

Date	Account Titles and Explanation	PR	Debit	Credit

GENERAL JOURNAL   Page____

Date	Account Titles and Explanation	PR	Debit	Credit

Chapter 14   Exercise 14-5   *Name* _____

_____

_____

_____

Exercise 14-6

	a.	b.	c.
PV of face amount			
PV of interest annuity			
Total issue price			

Calculations:

Name _____

a. _____

b. _____

c. _____
   _____

d.

PV of face amount .... _____

PV of interest annuity .... _____

Total issue price .... _____

Calculations:

e.   **GENERAL JOURNAL**   Page____

Date	Account Titles and Explanation	PR	Debit	Credit

a. Discount =
_____
_____

b. Total interest expense over the life of the bonds:
_____
_____
_____
_____
_____
_____
_____
_____

c. Amortization table:

Period Ending	Cash Interest Paid	Period Interest Expense	Discount Amort.	Unamortized Discount	Carrying Value

a. Amortization table:

Period Ending	Cash Interest Paid	Period Interest Expense	Discount Amort.	Unamortized Discount	Carrying Value

b.

GENERAL JOURNAL   Page_____

Date	Account Titles and Explanation	PR	Debit	Credit

a.

_____

_____

_____

_____

b. Amortization table:

Period Ending	Cash Interest Paid	Period Interest Expense	Discount Amort.	Unamortized Discount	Carrying Value

Exercise 14-11

a.

_____

_____

_____

_____

b. Amortization table:

Period Ending	Cash Interest Paid	Period Interest Expense	Discount Amort.	Unamortized Discount	Carrying Value

Name _____

Part 1   **GENERAL JOURNAL**   Page____

Date	Account Titles and Explanation	PR	Debit	Credit
a.				
b.				
c.				

Part 2

_____
_____
_____
_____
_____
_____
_____

Name _____

GENERAL JOURNAL   Page____

Date		Account Titles and Explanation	PR	Debit	Credit
a.					
b.					

Exercise 14-14

a. _____

b. _____

c. _____

_____

d.

PV of face amount .... _____

PV of interest annuity .... _____

Total issue price .... _____

Calculations:

e.   ## GENERAL JOURNAL   Page____

Date		Account Titles and Explanation	PR	Debit	Credit

a. _____

b. _____
_____
_____
_____
_____
_____

c. **Amortization table:**

Period Ending	Cash Interest Paid	Period Interest Expense	Premium Amort.	Unamortized Premium	Carrying Value

Calculations:

Name _____

a.

PV of face amount .... _____

PV of interest annuity .... _____

Total issue price .... _____

   Calculations:

b. Amortization table:

Period Ending	Cash Interest Paid	Period Interest Expense	Premium Amort.	Unamortized Premium	Carrying Value

Calculations:

Name _____

Part 1

a.   **GENERAL JOURNAL**   Page____

Date	Account Titles and Explanation	PR	Debit	Credit

b.   **GENERAL JOURNAL**   Page____

Date	Account Titles and Explanation	PR	Debit	Credit

c.   **GENERAL JOURNAL**   Page____

Date	Account Titles and Explanation	PR	Debit	Credit

Part 2

_____
_____
_____
_____
_____
_____

a.

PV of face amount .... _____

PV of interest annuity .... _____

Total issue price .... _____

Calculations:

b. Amortization table:

Period Ending	Cash Interest Paid	Period Interest Expense	Premium Amort.	Unamortized Premium	Carrying Value

Calculations:

Part 1

a.   **GENERAL JOURNAL**   Page____

Date	Account Titles and Explanation	PR	Debit	Credit

b.   **GENERAL JOURNAL**   Page____

Date	Account Titles and Explanation	PR	Debit	Credit

c.   **GENERAL JOURNAL**   Page____

Date	Account Titles and Explanation	PR	Debit	Credit

Part 2

_____
_____
_____
_____
_____

a.   **GENERAL JOURNAL**   Page____

Date	Account Titles and Explanation	PR	Debit	Credit

b.   **GENERAL JOURNAL**   Page____

Date	Account Titles and Explanation	PR	Debit	Credit

c.   **GENERAL JOURNAL**   Page____

Date	Account Titles and Explanation	PR	Debit	Credit

Exercise 14-21

1.   **GENERAL JOURNAL**   Page____

Date	Account Titles and Explanation	PR	Debit	Credit

2.

_____
_____
_____
_____
_____

1.

_____
_____
_____
_____
_____
_____

2.   **GENERAL JOURNAL**   Page____

Date	Account Titles and Explanation	PR	Debit	Credit

Exercise 14-23

a. _____
_____
_____

b. Amortization table:

Period Ending	(a) Beginning Balance Prior (e)	(b) Debit Interest Expense	(c) Debit Notes Payable	(d) Credit Cash (b) + (c)	(e) Ending Balance (a) – (c)
2018					
2019					
2020					
2021					
Total					

GENERAL JOURNAL

Page____

Date	Account Titles and Explanation	PR	Debit	Credit

a. _____

_____

b. **Amortization table:**

Period Ending	(a) Beginning Balance Prior (e)	(b) Debit Interest Expense	(c) Debit Notes Payable	(d) Credit Cash (b) + (c)	(e) Ending Balance (a) − (c)
2018					
2019					
2020					
2021					
Total					

Exercise 14-26

GENERAL JOURNAL   Page_____

Date	Account Titles and Explanation	PR	Debit	Credit

a.   **GENERAL JOURNAL**   Page____

Date	Account Titles and Explanation	PR	Debit	Credit

b.   **GENERAL JOURNAL**   Page____

Date	Account Titles and Explanation	PR	Debit	Credit

c.   **GENERAL JOURNAL**   Page____

Date	Account Titles and Explanation	PR	Debit	Credit

d.

(a) Year	(b) Beginning Net Liability	(c) Payment	(d) Interest Expense (b) × 10%	(e) Reduction in Lease Liability (c) − (d)	(f) Lease Liability at End of Year (b) − (e)
2018					
2019					
2020					
2021					
2022					
Total expense					

Name _____

	Solar Industries (in Millions)		Solar Financing Corp (in Millions)	
	2017	2016	2017	2016
Total Debt (A)				
Total Equity (B)				

Explanation

_____
_____
_____
_____
_____
_____
_____

Part 1

a.

PV of face amount ....

PV of interest annuity ....

Total issue price ....

b.   **GENERAL JOURNAL**   Page____

Date	Account Titles and Explanation	PR	Debit	Credit

Part 2

a.

PV of face amount ....   _____

PV of interest annuity ....   _____

Total issue price ....   _____

b.   **GENERAL JOURNAL**   Page____

Date	Account Titles and Explanation	PR	Debit	Credit

Part 3

a.

PV of face amount ....   _____

PV of interest annuity ....   _____

Total issue price ....   _____

3b.   **GENERAL JOURNAL**   Page____

Date	Account Titles and Explanation	PR	Debit	Credit

Chapter 14   Problem 14-2A   *Name* _____

1.

PV of face amount .... _____
PV of interest annuity .... _____
Total issue price .... _____

2.   **GENERAL JOURNAL**   Page____

Date	Account Titles and Explanation	PR	Debit	Credit

3.

_____
_____
_____
_____
_____
_____
_____
_____
_____
_____

4. Amortization table:

Period Ending	Cash Interest Paid	Period Interest Expense	Discount Amort.	Unamortized Discount	Carrying Value

5.   **GENERAL JOURNAL**   Page____

Date	Account Titles and Explanation	PR	Debit	Credit

Analysis component:

_____
_____
_____
_____
_____
_____
_____
_____
_____
_____
_____
_____
_____
_____
_____

Name

1.

PV of face amount ....

PV of interest annuity ....

Total issue price ....

2. Amortization table:

Period Ending	Cash Interest Paid	Period Interest Expense	Discount Amort.	Unamortized Discount	Carrying Value

Calculations:

Chapter 14   Problem 14-4A   *Name*_____

Part 1 a.   GENERAL JOURNAL   Page____

Date	Account Titles and Explanation	PR	Debit	Credit

b.   GENERAL JOURNAL   Page____

Date	Account Titles and Explanation	PR	Debit	Credit

c.   GENERAL JOURNAL   Page____

Date	Account Titles and Explanation	PR	Debit	Credit

d.   GENERAL JOURNAL   Page____

Date	Account Titles and Explanation	PR	Debit	Credit

Part 2

_____
_____
_____
_____
_____

Part 1.

_____
_____
_____
_____
_____
_____
_____

Part 2.

Period Ending	Cash Interest Paid	Period Interest Expense	Premium Amort.	Unamortized Premium	Carrying Value

Part 3.   GENERAL JOURNAL   Page____

Date	Account Titles and Explanation	PR	Debit	Credit

Part 4.

PV of face amount .... _____

PV of interest annuity .... _____

Total issue price .... _____

Chapter 14   Problem 14-6A   *Name* _____

Part 1

a.

_____

_____

_____

b.

Period Ending	Cash Interest Paid	Period Interest Expense	Premium Amort.	Unamortized Premium	Carrying Value

c.   **GENERAL JOURNAL**   Page____

Date	Account Titles and Explanation	PR	Debit	Credit

Part 2

a.

_____

_____

_____

_____

b.

Period Ending	Cash Interest Paid	Period Interest Expense	Discount Amort.	Unamortized Discount	Carrying Value

c. & d.

GENERAL JOURNAL

Page_____

Date	Account Titles and Explanation	PR	Debit	Credit

Name _____

Bond Issue A:

a. _____

b.   **GENERAL JOURNAL**   Page____

Date	Account Titles and Explanation	PR	Debit	Credit

c. _____

d. _____

e. _____

f. _____
_____
_____
_____
_____

g. _____
_____
_____
_____
_____

h.   **GENERAL JOURNAL**   Page____

Date	Account Titles and Explanation	PR	Debit	Credit

Bond Issue B:

a. _____

b.   **GENERAL JOURNAL**   Page____

Date	Account Titles and Explanation	PR	Debit	Credit

c. _____

d. _____

e. _____

f. _____

g. _____

h. _____

.   **GENERAL JOURNAL**   Page____

Date	Account Titles and Explanation	PR	Debit	Credit

Chapter 14   Problem 14-8A   *Name* _____

Part 1

_____

_____

_____

_____

_____

Part 2

	(a)	(b)	Payments	(d)	(e)
	Beginning		(c)		Ending
Period	Balance	Debit Interest	Debit Notes Payable	Credit Cash	Balance
Ending	Prior (e)	Expense	(d) – (b)	(b) + (c)	(a) – (c)

_____

_____

_____

_____

_____

_____

3.   **GENERAL JOURNAL**   Page_____

Date	Account Titles and Explanation	PR	Debit	Credit

Part 4

	(a)	(b)	Payments	(d)	(e)
	Beginning		(c)		Ending
Period	Balance	Debit Interest	Debit Notes Payable	Credit Cash	Balance
Ending	Prior (e)	Expense	(d) – (b)	(b) + (c)	(a) – (c)

_____

_____

_____

_____

_____

_____

GENERAL JOURNAL   Page____

Date	Account Titles and Explanation	PR	Debit	Credit

Problem 14-9A

Part 1
_____

Part 2

(a) Year	(b) Lease liability at the start of year	(c) Payment	(d) Interest Expense	(e) Reduction in Lease Liability (c) – (d)	(f) Lease Liability at End of Year (b) – (e)
2017					
2018					
2019					
2020					
Total expense					

Part 3   GENERAL JOURNAL   Page____

Date	Account Titles and Explanation	PR	Debit	Credit

Part 4   **GENERAL JOURNAL**   Page____

Date	Account Titles and Explanation	PR	Debit	Credit

LAPORTE ENGINEERING COMPANY

Partial Balance Sheet

December 31, 2018

Chapter 14   Problem 14-1B   *Name* _____

Part 1a.
PV of face amount .... _____
PV of interest annuity .... _____
Total issue price .... _____

b.   **GENERAL JOURNAL**   Page____

Date	Account Titles and Explanation	PR	Debit	Credit

Part 2a.
PV of face amount .... _____
PV of interest annuity .... _____
Total issue price .... _____

b.   **GENERAL JOURNAL**   Page____

Date	Account Titles and Explanation	PR	Debit	Credit

Part 3a.
PV of face amount .... _____
PV of interest annuity .... _____
Total issue price .... _____

b.   **GENERAL JOURNAL**   Page____

Date	Account Titles and Explanation	PR	Debit	Credit

Name _____

Part 1   **GENERAL JOURNAL**   Page____

Date	Account Titles and Explanation	PR	Debit	Credit

Part 2

_____

_____

_____

_____

_____

_____

Part 3 - Amortization table:

Period Ending	Cash Interest Paid	Period Interest Expense	Discount Amort.	Unamortized Discount	Carrying Value
Jan. 01/17					
Jun. 30/17					
Dec. 31/17					

Part 4   **GENERAL JOURNAL**   Page____

Date	Account Titles and Explanation	PR	Debit	Credit

Name _____

a. _____
_____
_____
_____
_____
_____
_____

b. Amortization table:

Period Ending	Cash Interest Paid	Period Interest Expense	Premium Amort.	Unamortized Premium	Carrying Value

Calculations:

Name _____

Part 1a.   **GENERAL JOURNAL**   Page____

Date	Account Titles and Explanation	PR	Debit	Credit

b.   **GENERAL JOURNAL**   Page____

Date	Account Titles and Explanation	PR	Debit	Credit

c.   **GENERAL JOURNAL**   Page____

Date	Account Titles and Explanation	PR	Debit	Credit

Part 2.

_____

_____

_____

_____

_____

Chapter 14   Problem 14-5B   *Name*

Part 1

Part 2

Period Ending	Cash Interest Paid	Period Interest Expense	Discount Amort.	Unamortized Discount	Carrying Value

Calculations:

Part 3   GENERAL JOURNAL   Page____

Date	Account Titles and Explanation	PR	Debit	Credit

Part 4

_____
_____
_____
_____
_____
_____
_____
_____
_____
_____
_____

Problem 14-6B

Part 1

a. _____
_____
_____
_____

b.

Period Ending	Cash Interest Paid	Period Interest Expense	Discount Amort.	Unamortized Discount	Carrying Value

Calculations:

c. & d.   **GENERAL JOURNAL**   Page_____

Date	Account Titles and Explanation	PR	Debit	Credit

Part 2

a.

_____
_____
_____
_____

b.

Period Ending	Cash Interest Paid	Period Interest Expense	Premium Amort.	Unamortized Premium	Carrying Value

c.   **GENERAL JOURNAL**   Page____

Date	Account Titles and Explanation	PR	Debit	Credit

Calculations:

Chapter 14   Problem 14-7B   *Name* _____

Bond Issue 1:
a. _____

b.   **GENERAL JOURNAL**   Page____

Date	Account Titles and Explanation	PR	Debit	Credit

c. _____

d. _____

e. _____

f. _____

g. _____

h. _____

i.   **GENERAL JOURNAL**   Page____

Date	Account Titles and Explanation	PR	Debit	Credit

Bond Issue 2:

a. _____

b.   GENERAL JOURNAL   Page____

Date	Account Titles and Explanation	PR	Debit	Credit

c. _____

d. _____

e. _____

f. _____

g. _____

_____

_____

_____

h. _____

_____

_____

_____

i.   GENERAL JOURNAL   Page____

Date	Account Titles and Explanation	PR	Debit	Credit

Name _____

Part 1

_____
_____
_____
_____
_____
_____
_____
_____
_____
_____

Part 2

Period Ending	(a) Beginning Balance Prior (e)	(b) Debit Interest Expense	(c) Debit Notes Payable (d) – (b)	(d) Credit Cash (b) + (c)	(e) Ending Balance (a) – (c)

Part 3.   **GENERAL JOURNAL**   Page____

Date	Account Titles and Explanation	PR	Debit	Credit

Part 4

Period Ending	(a) Beginning Balance Prior (e)	(b) Debit Interest Expense	(c) Debit Notes Payable (d) – (b)	(d) Credit Cash (b) + (c)	(e) Ending Balance (a) – (c)

GENERAL JOURNAL   Page____

Date	Account Titles and Explanation	PR	Debit	Credit

Chapter 14   Problem 14-9B   *Name* _____

Part 1

_____

Part 2

(a) Year	(b) Lease liability at the start of year	(c) Payment	(d) Interest Expense (b) × 9%	(e) Reduction in Lease Liability (c) – (d)	(f) Lease Liability at End of Year (b) – (e)
2017					
2018					
2019					
2020					
2021					
2022					
Total expense					

Part 3   GENERAL JOURNAL   Page____

Date	Account Titles and Explanation	PR	Debit	Credit

Part 4   GENERAL JOURNAL   Page____

Date	Account Titles and Explanation	PR	Debit	Credit

PEERLESS CARPET CORP
Partial Balance Sheet
December 31, 2018

Name _____

(1) _____
(2) _____
(3) _____
(4) _____
(5) _____
(6) _____
(7) _____
(8) _____

Explanations:

_____
_____
_____
_____
_____
_____

Quick Study 15-2

(1) _____
(2) _____
(3) _____
(4) _____
(5) _____
(6) _____
(7) _____
(8) _____

Quick Study 15-3

GENERAL JOURNAL   Page____

Date	Account Titles and Explanation	PR	Debit	Credit

Name _____

GENERAL JOURNAL   Page____

Date	Account Titles and Explanation	PR	Debit	Credit

Calculations:

_____
_____
_____
_____
_____
_____
_____
_____

Quick Study 15-5

GENERAL JOURNAL   Page____

Date	Account Titles and Explanation	PR	Debit	Credit

Calculations:

_____
_____
_____
_____
_____
_____
_____
_____

_____
_____
_____
_____

Quick Study 15-7

GENERAL JOURNAL   Page____

Date		Account Titles and Explanation	PR	Debit	Credit

Name _____

GENERAL JOURNAL   Page____

Date	Account Titles and Explanation	PR	Debit	Credit

Name _____

GENERAL JOURNAL   Page____

Date		Account Titles and Explanation	PR	Debit	Credit

Quick Study 15-10

_____

_____

_____

_____

Name _____

GENERAL JOURNAL   Page____

Date	Account Titles and Explanation	PR	Debit	Credit

Quick Study 15-12

GENERAL JOURNAL   Page____

Date	Account Titles and Explanation	PR	Debit	Credit

Name _____

GENERAL JOURNAL   Page____

Date		Account Titles and Explanation	PR	Debit	Credit

GENERAL JOURNAL   Page____

Date	Account Titles and Explanation	PR	Debit	Credit

Calculations:

Investments	Unadjusted Balance at Dec. 31/17	Fair Values at Dec. 31/17	Difference

Analysis component:

_____
_____
_____
_____
_____
_____
_____
_____
_____
_____

Exercise 15-2

GENERAL JOURNAL   Page____

Date	Account Titles and Explanation	PR	Debit	Credit

GENERAL JOURNAL   Page____

Date	Account Titles and Explanation	PR	Debit	Credit

Calculations:

Investments	Unadjusted Balance at Dec. 31/17	Fair Values at Dec. 31/17	Difference

Analysis component:

_____
_____
_____
_____
_____
_____
_____
_____
_____
_____

Exercise 15-3
Part 1   GENERAL JOURNAL   Page____

Date	Account Titles and Explanation	PR	Debit	Credit

Calculations:

	Cost	Fair Value	Difference

Part 2

_____
_____
_____

Part 1   **GENERAL JOURNAL**   Page____

Date	Account Titles and Explanation	PR	Debit	Credit

Part 2

International Journalist Corporation
Partial Balance Sheet
December 31, 2017

International Journalist Corporation
Partial Balance Sheet
December 31, 2018

Exercise 15-5

Part 1 – Partial Amortization Schedule – Hanna Corporation Bond:

Period Ending	Cash Interest Received	Period Interest Income	Premium Amort.	Unamortized Premium	Carrying Value

Part 1 cont'd. – Partial Amortization Schedule – Trust Inc Bond:

Period Ending	Cash Interest Received	Period Interest Income	Discount Amort.	Unamortized Discount	Carrying Value

Part 2

GENERAL JOURNAL

Page____

Date	Account Titles and Explanation	PR	Debit	Credit

Part 3

Corona Inc.	
Partial Balance Sheet	
December 31, 2017	

Exercise 15-6

Part 1

Period Ending	Cash Interest Received	Period Interest Income	Premium Amort.	Unamortized Premium	Carrying Value

Part 2

GENERAL JOURNAL   Page____

Date	Account Titles and Explanation	PR	Debit	Credit

GENERAL JOURNAL   Page_____

Date	Account Titles and Explanation	PR	Debit	Credit

Part 3

George's Mortgage Inc.	
Partial Balance Sheet	
December 31, 2017	

Exercise 15-7

_____

_____

_____

GENERAL JOURNAL   Page____

Date	Account Titles and Explanation	PR	Debit	Credit

Book value

_____
_____
_____
_____
_____
_____
_____
_____
_____
_____
_____
_____
_____
_____
_____
_____

Problem 15-1A

Part 1

Period Ending	Cash Interest Received	Period Interest Income	Premium Amort.	Unamortized Premium	Carrying Value

Part 2   **GENERAL JOURNAL**   Page_____

Date	Account Titles and Explanation	PR	Debit	Credit

GENERAL JOURNAL   Page____

Date	Account Titles and Explanation	PR	Debit	Credit

GENERAL JOURNAL   Page____

Date	Account Titles and Explanation	PR	Debit	Credit

Calculations:

	Cost	Fair Value	Difference

Part 3

Landers Inc.
Partial Balance Sheet
December 31, 2017

Analysis component:

_____

_____

_____

_____

_____

_____

Name _____

Part 1

Period Ending	Cash Interest Received	Period Interest Income	Discount Amort.	Unamortized Discount	Carrying Value

Part 2   **GENERAL JOURNAL**   Page____

Date	Account Titles and Explanation	PR	Debit	Credit

GENERAL JOURNAL

Date	Account Titles and Explanation	PR	Debit	Credit

GENERAL JOURNAL

Date	Account Titles and Explanation	PR	Debit	Credit

Calculations:

	Cost	Fair Value	Difference

Part 3

Safety Development Corporation
Partial Balance Sheet
December 31, 2017

Analysis component:

Part 1

Period Ending	Cash Interest Received	Period Interest Income	Premium Amort.	Unamortized Premium	Carrying Value

Part 2(a) GENERAL JOURNAL Page____

Date	Account Titles and Explanation	PR	Debit	Credit

Part 2(b) GENERAL JOURNAL Page____

Date	Account Titles and Explanation	PR	Debit	Credit

Part 3

Liu Corporation		
Partial Balance Sheet		
December 31, 2017		

Problem 15-4A

GENERAL JOURNAL   Page____

Date	Account Titles and Explanation	PR	Debit	Credit

GENERAL JOURNAL   Page____

Date	Account Titles and Explanation	PR	Debit	Credit

Analysis component:
_____
_____
_____
_____
_____
_____
_____
_____

Problem 15-5A

Part 1   ## GENERAL JOURNAL   Page____

Date	Account Titles and Explanation	PR	Debit	Credit

Part 1   **GENERAL JOURNAL**   Page____

Date	Account Titles and Explanation	PR	Debit	Credit

Calculations:

_____
_____
_____
_____
_____
_____
_____
_____
_____
_____
_____
_____
_____

Part 2

_____
_____

Part 3

_____
_____
_____
_____
_____
_____
_____

Name _____

Part 1

Period Ending	Cash Interest Received	Period Interest Income	Discount Amort.	Unamortized Discount	Carrying Value

Part 2   **GENERAL JOURNAL**   Page____

Date	Account Titles and Explanation	PR	Debit	Credit

GENERAL JOURNAL

Page____

Date	Account Titles and Explanation	PR	Debit	Credit

GENERAL JOURNAL

Page_____

Date	Account Titles and Explanation	PR	Debit	Credit

Calculations:

	Cost	Fair Value	Difference

Part 3

Huang Hardware Inc.
Partial Balance Sheet
December 31, 2017

Analysis component:

Chapter 15 Problem 15-2B

Name _____

Part 1

Period Ending	Cash Interest Received	Period Interest Income	Premium Amort.	Unamortized Premium	Carrying Value

Part 2

GENERAL JOURNAL

Page____

Date	Account Titles and Explanation	PR	Debit	Credit

GENERAL JOURNAL

Page____

Date		Account Titles and Explanation	PR	Debit	Credit

GENERAL JOURNAL   Page____

Date	Account Titles and Explanation	PR	Debit	Credit

Calculations:

	Cost	Fair Value	Difference

Part 3

Thornhill Corporation
Partial Balance Sheet
December 31, 2017

Analysis component:

Problem 15-3B   *Name* _____

Part 1

Period Ending	Cash Interest Received	Period Interest Income	Discount Amort.	Unamortized Discount	Carrying Value

Part 2(a)   **GENERAL JOURNAL**   Page____

Date	Account Titles and Explanation	PR	Debit	Credit

Chapter 15   Problem 15-3B (concl'd.)

Part 2(b)   **GENERAL JOURNAL**   Page____

Date	Account Titles and Explanation	PR	Debit	Credit

Part 3

JoeLite Corporation
Partial Balance Sheet
December 31, 2017

Problem 15-4B Part 1

_____

_____

_____

_____

_____

_____

Non-strategic Investments:

	Cost	Fair Value	Difference

Part 2   **GENERAL JOURNAL**   Page____

Date	Account Titles and Explanation	PR	Debit	Credit

Name _____

GENERAL JOURNAL   Page____

Date	Account Titles and Explanation	PR	Debit	Credit

Part 2

_____

_____

Part 3

_____

_____

_____

_____

_____

_____

_____

_____

Name _____

(1) _____   (6) _____
(2) _____   (7) _____
(3) _____   (8) _____
(4) _____   (9) _____
(5) _____   (10) _____

Quick Study 16-2

(1) _____   (5) _____
(2) _____   (6) _____
(3) _____   (7) _____
(4) _____   (8) _____

Quick Study 16-3

(1) _____

_____

(2) _____

_____

(3) _____

_____

(4) _____

_____

(5) _____

_____

(6) _____

_____

Quick Study 16-4

_____
_____
_____
_____
_____
_____

Quick Study 16-6

Quick Study 16-7

Quick Study 16-9

a. _____   **Equipment**

_____
_____
_____
_____
_____
_____

b. _____   **Accumulated Deprec., Equipment**

_____
_____
_____
_____
_____

GENERAL JOURNAL   Page____

Date	Account Titles and Explanation	PR	Debit	Credit

a. _____
_____
_____
_____

b. _____
_____
_____
_____

Calculations:

Equipment		Accumulated Deprec., Equipment

GENERAL JOURNAL   Page____

Date	Account Titles and Explanation	PR	Debit	Credit

c. _____
_____
_____
_____

a.

Common Shares

b.

Notes Payable, Long-Term

c.

Retained Earnings

Body content absent.

Chapter 16   Quick Study 16-12   *Name*

a.

Retained Earnings

b.

Common Shares

c.

Notes Payable, Long-Term

d.

Name _____

PARKER CONSULTING
Statement of Cash Flows
For Year Ended March 31, 2017

SUGAR BAKERY INC.
Statement of Cash Flows
For Year Ended October 31, 2017

_____
_____
_____
_____

Quick Study 16-16

_____
_____
_____
_____
_____

Quick Study 16-17

_____
_____
_____
_____
_____

Quick Study 16-18

a.
_____
_____
_____
_____
_____
_____
_____

b.
_____
_____
_____
_____
_____

c.
_____
_____
_____
_____
_____
_____

Name _____

a. _____   **Accounts Receivable**

_____

_____

_____

_____

_____

_____

_____

_____

b. _____

_____

_____

_____

_____

Inventory   **Accounts Payable**

c. _____

_____

_____

_____

d. _____

_____

_____

_____

e. _____

	Statement of Cash Flows			*Footnote describing Non-Cash Investing & Financing Activities*	*Not Reported on Statement or in Footnote*
	Operating Activities	*Investing Activities*	*Financing Activities*		
a. Land was purchased by issuing common shares.					
b. Recorded depreciation expense.					
c. Income taxes payable increased by 15% from prior year.					
d. Declared and paid a cash dividend.					
e. Paid cash to purchase inventory.					
f. Sold equipment at a loss.					
g. Accounts receivable decreased during the year.					

Exercise 16-2

		Adjust by	
Adjustments to derive cash flow from operating activities:		*Adding*	*Subtracting*
1. Changes in non-cash current assets:			
a. Increases		_____	_____
b. Decreases		_____	_____
2. Changes in current liabilities:			
a. Increases		_____	_____
b. Decreases		_____	_____
3. Depreciation of plant and equipment		_____	_____
4. Amortization of intangible assets		_____	_____
5. Interest expense:			
a. Bond Premium amortized		_____	_____
b. Bond Discount amortized		_____	_____
6. Sale of non-current asset:			
a. Gain		_____	_____
b. Loss		_____	_____

Part 1

Part 2

_____

Exercise 16-4

Name _____

_____
_____
_____
_____
_____
_____
_____
_____
_____
_____
_____
_____
_____
_____
_____
_____
_____

Exercise 16-6

WESTERN ENVIRONMENTAL INC.
Statement of Cash Flows
For Year Ended June 30, 2017

Name

(1)

(2)

(3)

(4)

(5)

Equipment	Accumulated Depreciation, Equipment

(6) _____
_____
_____
_____
_____

(7) _____
_____
_____
_____

WESTERN ENVIRONMENTAL INC.
Statement of Cash Flows
For Year Ended June 30, 2017

	Statement of Cash Flows			Footnote describing Non-Cash Investing & Financing Activities	Not Reported on Statement or in Footnote
	Operating Activities	Investing Activities	Financing Activities		
a. Long-term bonds payable were retired by issuing common shares.					
b. Surplus merchandise inventory was sold for cash.					
c. Borrowed cash from the bank by signing a nine-month note payable.					
d. Paid cash to purchase a patent.					
e. A six-month note receivable was accepted in exchange for a building that had been used in operations.					
f. Recorded depreciation expense on all plant assets.					
g. A cash dividend that had been declared in a previous period was paid in the current period.					

Case A		
Case B		
Case C		

Case A		

Case B		

Case C		

Analysis component:

Name _____

ROSETTA INC.
Statement of Cash Flows
For Year Ended December 31, 2017

Note disclosure: _____

_____

_____

_____

_____

_____

ZEBRA CORPORATION
Statement of Cash Flows
For Year Ended December 31, 2017

Analysis component:

LAG NETWORK INC.
Statement of Cash Flows
For Year Ended December 31, 2017

Analysis component:

_____
_____
_____
_____
_____
_____
_____

Name _____

LAG NETWORK INC.
Statement of Cash Flows
For Year Ended December 31, 2017

Supporting calculations:

Chapter 16   Problem 16-3A   *Name* _____

Part 1

_____
_____
_____
_____
_____
_____

Part 2	**UNION BRAKE INC.**		
	Statement of Cash Flows		
	For Year Ended December 31, 2017		

Analysis component:

_____
_____
_____
_____
_____
_____

UNION BRAKE INC.

Statement of Cash Flows

For Year Ended December 31, 2017

Calculations:

Name _____

ICE DRILLING INC.
Statement of Cash Flows
For Year Ended December 31, 2017

Note disclosure: _____

_____

_____

_____

_____

_____

Analysis component:

_____

_____

_____

_____

_____

_____

_____

_____

_____

_____

_____

_____

_____

_____

_____

_____

_____

_____

_____

_____

_____

ICE DRILLING INC.
Statement of Cash Flows
For Year Ended December 31, 2017

Note disclosure:

Supporting calculations:

_____
_____
_____
_____
_____
_____
_____
_____
_____
_____
_____
_____
_____
_____
_____
_____
_____

Problem 16-7A

PADDLEBOARD INC.
Statement of Cash Flows
For Year Ended December 31, 2017

Supporting calculations:

_____
_____
_____
_____
_____
_____
_____
_____
_____
_____
_____
_____
_____
_____

Analysis component:

_____
_____
_____
_____
_____
_____
_____
_____
_____
_____
_____
_____
_____

Name _____

PADDLEBOARD INC.
Statement of Cash Flows
For Year Ended December 31, 2017

Supporting calculations: _____

_____

_____

_____

_____

_____

_____

_____

_____

_____

_____

_____

Fundamental Accounting Principles, **15ce, Working Papers**

Name _____

LOCK & KEY INC.
Statement of Cash Flows
For Year Ended December 31, 2017
(000s)

Supporting calculations:

_____
_____
_____
_____
_____
_____
_____
_____
_____
_____
_____
_____
_____
_____
_____
_____

Analysis component:

_____
_____
_____
_____
_____
_____
_____
_____
_____

Name _____

LOCK & KEY INC.
Statement of Cash Flows
For Year Ended December 31, 2017
(000s)

Supporting calculations:

Name _____

SUNNY TECHNOLOGIES INC.
Statement of Cash Flows
For Year Ended December 31, 2017

Note disclosure: _____

_____

_____

_____

_____

_____

_____

Fundamental Accounting Principles, 15ce, Working Papers

Supporting calculations:

_____
_____
_____
_____
_____
_____
_____
_____
_____
_____
_____
_____
_____
_____
_____
_____

Analysis component:

_____
_____
_____
_____
_____
_____
_____
_____
_____
_____

Name _____

SUNNY TECHNOLOGIES INC.
Statement of Cash Flows
For Year Ended December 31, 2017

Note disclosure: _____

Supporting calculations: _____

Name

MED SUPPLIES INC.
Statement of Cash Flows
For Year Ended December 31, 2017

Analysis component:

Name _____

MED SUPPLIES INC.
Statement of Cash Flows
For Year Ended December 31, 2017

Supporting calculations:

_____
_____
_____
_____
_____
_____
_____

Fundamental Accounting Principles, 15ce, Working Papers

Name _____

Part 1

_____
_____
_____
_____
_____

Part 2

BURROW MINING INC.
Statement of Cash Flows
For Year Ended December 31, 2017

Analysis component:

_____
_____
_____
_____
_____
_____

BURROW MINING INC.
Statement of Cash Flows
For Year Ended December 31, 2017

Supporting calculations:

Name _____

TRIPLE FLIP INC.
Statement of Cash Flows
For Year Ended December 31, 2017

Note disclosure: _____

_____

_____

_____

_____

Supporting calculations: _____

_____

_____

_____

_____

_____

_____

_____

_____

_____

_____

_____

_____

_____

_____

_____

_____

Analysis component: _____

_____

_____

_____

_____

_____

_____

_____

_____

_____

_____

_____

_____

_____

Name _____

TRIPLE FLIP INC.
Statement of Cash Flows
For Year Ended December 31, 2017

Note disclosure: _____

_____

_____

_____

_____

Supporting calculations: _____

_____

_____

_____

_____

_____

_____

_____

_____

_____

_____

_____

_____

_____

_____

_____

_____

_____

Problem 16-7B

ZHANG SYSTEMS INC.		
Statement of Cash Flows		
For Year Ended December 31, 2017		
(millions of dollars)		

Supporting calculations:

_____
_____
_____
_____
_____
_____
_____
_____
_____
_____
_____
_____
_____
_____
_____
_____
_____
_____

Analysis component:

_____
_____
_____
_____
_____
_____
_____
_____
_____
_____
_____
_____
_____
_____

Name

ZHANG SYSTEMS INC.
Statement of Cash Flows
For Year Ended December 31, 2017
(millions of dollars)

Supporting calculations:

Name _____

CLEAR STRATEGY CORP.
Statement of Cash Flows
For Year Ended December 31, 2017
(millions of dollars)

Note disclosure:

_____
_____
_____
_____
_____
_____

Supporting calculations:

_____
_____
_____
_____
_____
_____
_____
_____
_____
_____
_____
_____
_____

Analysis component:

_____
_____
_____
_____
_____
_____
_____
_____
_____
_____
_____
_____
_____

CLEAR STRATEGY CORP.
Statement of Cash Flows
For Year Ended December 31, 2017
(millions of dollars)

Note disclosure: _____

_____

_____

Supporting calculations: _____

_____

_____

_____

_____

COUNTRY FEED INC.
Statement of Cash Flows
For Year Ended December 31, 2017

Note disclosure:

Supporting calculations:

_____
_____
_____
_____
_____
_____
_____
_____
_____
_____
_____
_____
_____
_____

Analysis component:

_____
_____
_____
_____
_____
_____
_____
_____
_____
_____
_____

COUNTRY FEED INC.

Statement of Cash Flows

For Year Ended December 31, 2017

Note disclosure: _____

_____

Supporting calculations: _____

_____
_____
_____
_____
_____
_____
_____

Name _____

Quick Study 17-2

Quick Study 17-3

Item	Dollar Change	Base Amount	Percent Change
Current non-strategic investments			
Accounts receivable			
Notes payable			

	2017	*2016*	*2015*	*2014*	*2013*
Sales					
Cost of goods sold					
Accounts receivable					

_____
_____
_____
_____
_____
_____

Quick Study 17-5

	2017	*2016*
Sales		
Cost of goods sold		
Gross profit from sales		
Operating expenses		
Profit		

_____
_____
_____
_____
_____
_____

CARMON CUPCAKE INC.
Common-Size Comparative Balance Sheet
December 31

	2017	2016	2015

Quick Study 17-7

(a)

(b)

(c)

(d)

Quick Study 17-8

(a)

(b)

	2017	2016
Accounts receivable turnover		

_____
_____
_____
_____
_____
_____
_____
_____

Quick Study 17-10

	2017	2016
Days' sales uncollected		

_____
_____
_____
_____
_____
_____
_____
_____

Quick Study 17-11

_____
_____
_____
_____
_____
_____
_____
_____
_____
_____
_____

Name _____

a.	Company A	Company B	Company C

b.
_____

Quick Study 17-13
_____
_____
_____
_____

Quick Study 17-14

	2017	2016	2015

Calculations and analysis:
_____
_____
_____
_____
_____
_____
_____
_____
_____

	Company A	*Company B*	*Company C*	*Least Favourable*
Debt ratio				
Equity ratio				
Pledged assets to secured liabilities				

Explanations:

_____
_____
_____
_____
_____
_____
_____
_____
_____
_____
_____
_____
_____
_____
_____
_____
_____
_____
_____

Chapter 17   Quick Study 17-16   *Name* _____

_____
_____
_____
_____
_____
_____

Quick Study 17-17

_____
_____
_____
_____
_____

Quick Study 17-18

_____
_____
_____
_____
_____

Quick Study 17-19

_____
_____
_____
_____
_____

Quick Study 17-20

_____
_____
_____
_____
_____

Quick Study 17-21

_____
_____
_____
_____
_____
_____

_____
_____
_____
_____
_____
_____

Quick Study 17-23

Part a.

	ABC Inc.	XYZ Inc.
Price-earnings ratio		

b. _____

Quick Study 17-24

a. _____

_____

b. _____

_____

Exercise 17-1

_____
_____
_____
_____
_____
_____
_____
_____
_____
_____
_____
_____
_____
_____
_____
_____

Chapter 17   Exercise 17-2   *Name* _____

a.

	Current Assets	Current Liabilities	Current Ratio	Comparison to Industry Norm (F or U)
Company 1	$78,000	$31,000		
Company 2	114,000	75,000		
Company 3	60,000	99,000		

b. _____

c. _____

Analysis component:

_____

_____

_____

_____

_____

_____

_____

Exercise 17-3

a.

	#1	#2	#3
Current ratio			
Quick ratio			

b. _____

_____

_____

_____

_____

_____

_____

_____

_____

_____

_____

	2017	2016
Accounts receivable turnover		

_____
_____
_____
_____
_____
_____
_____
_____
_____
_____
_____

Exercise 17-5

a.	2017	2016	2015
Days' sales uncollected			

_____
_____
_____
_____
_____
_____

b. _____
_____
_____
_____
_____
_____
_____
_____

Name _____

a.

	Computer Inc.		Furniture Retailers		Freshcut Flowers Inc.		Custom Furniture Corp	
	2017	2016	2017	2016	2017	2016	2017	2016
Cost of goods sold	$1,350	$960	$2,940	$1,920	$2,160	$2,430	$2,190	$1,740
Inventory	150	120	105	60	15	9	45	120
2014 Merchandise turnover								

b. _____
_____
_____
_____
_____

c. _____
_____
_____
_____

Exercise 17-7

	Furniture Retailers	Custom Furniture Corp
Days' sales in inventory		

_____
_____
_____
_____
_____

Ratio	Calculations	
	2017	2016
Current ratio		

Favourable or unfavourable and why:

_____
_____
_____

Ratio	Calculations	
	2017	2016
Quick ratio		

Favourable or unfavourable and why:

_____
_____
_____

Ratio	Calculations	
	2017	2016
Accounts receivable turnover		

Favourable or unfavourable and why:

_____
_____
_____

Ratio	Calculations	
	2017	2016
Days' sales uncollected		

Favourable or unfavourable and why:

_____
_____
_____

Ratio	Calculations	
	2017	2016
Inventory turnover		

Favourable or unfavourable and why: _____

_____

_____

_____

_____

Ratio	Calculations	
	2017	2016
Days' sales in inventory		

Favourable or unfavourable and why: _____

_____

_____

_____

Ratio	Calculations	
	2017	2016
Total asset turnover		

Favourable or unfavourable and why: _____

_____

_____

_____

Ratio	Calculations	
	2017	2016
Accounts payable turnover		

Favourable or unfavourable and why: _____

_____

_____

_____

Name _____

Ratio	Calculations	
	2017	2016
Debt ratio		

Favourable or unfavourable and why:

_____

_____

_____

Ratio	Calculations	
	2017	2016
Equity ratio		

Favourable or unfavourable and why:

_____

_____

_____

Ratio	Calculations	
	2017	2016
Pledged assets to secured liabilities		

Favourable or unfavourable and why:

_____

_____

_____

Ratio	Calculations	
	2017	2016
Times interest earned		

Favourable or unfavourable and why:

_____

_____

_____

Name _____

	2017	Industry Average	F/U
Profit margin		14%	
Gross profit ratio		18%	
Return on total assets		20%	
Return on common shareholders' equity		32.7%	
Book value per common share		$8.63	
Book value per preferred share		$15.00	
Earnings per share		$1.79	

Analysis component:

	2017	2016	2015	F/U
Sales				
Accounts receivable				
Cost of goods sold				
Accounts payable				

_____
_____
_____
_____
_____
_____
_____
_____
_____
_____
_____
_____

Exercise 17-11

	Grant Inc.	Singh Inc.
Pledged assets		
Secured liabilities		
Ratio		

_____
_____
_____
_____
_____

Exercise 17-12

	2017	2016
Return on total assets		

_____
_____
_____
_____
_____

Chapter 17   Exercise 17-13   Part 1   *Name* _____

Spence Resources Inc.
Balance Sheet
December 31

	2017	2016	2015

Part 2	2017	2016	Favourable or Unfavourable
Return on common shareholders' equity			
Price-earnings			
Dividend yield			

Name _____

a. _____
_____
_____
_____
_____
_____
_____

b. _____
_____
_____
_____
_____
_____
_____
_____

Exercise 17-15

1. _____

2. _____

3. _____
_____
_____
_____
_____
_____

4. _____
_____
_____
_____
_____
_____
_____
_____
_____
_____
_____
_____

5. _____

_____
_____
_____
_____
_____
_____
_____
_____
_____
_____
_____

Analysis component: _____

_____
_____
_____
_____
_____
_____
_____
_____
_____
_____
_____
_____

URANIUM MINING CORPORATION
Income Statement Trends
For Years Ended December 31, 2011–2017

	2017	2016	2015	2014	2013	2012	2011
Net sales							
Cost of goods sold							
Gross profit							
Operating expenses							
Profit							

URANIUM MINING CORPORATION
Balance Sheet Trends
December 31, 2011–2017

	2017	2016	2015	2014	2013	2012	2011
Cash							
Accounts receivable, net							
Inventory							
Other current assets							
Long-term investments							
Plant and equip., net							
Total assets							
Current liabilities							
Non-current liabilities							
Common shares							
Retained earnings							
Total liabilities and equity							

Analysis component:

_____
_____
_____
_____
_____
_____
_____
_____
_____
_____
_____
_____
_____
_____
_____
_____
_____

	2017	2016	2015
1. Current ratio:			

2.

INDEPENDENT AUTO INC.
Common-Size Comparative Income Statement
For Years Ended December 31, 2017, 2016, and 2015

	2017	2016	2015
Net sales			
Cost of goods sold			
Gross profit from sales			
Selling expenses			
Administrative expenses			
Total operating expenses			
Profit before taxes			
Income taxes			
Profit			

3.

INDEPENDENT AUTO INC.
Balance Sheet Data in Trend Percentages
December 31, 2017, 2016, and 2015

	2017	2016	2015
Assets			
Current assets			
Non-strategic investments ...			
Plant and equipment			
Total assets			
Liabilities and Equity			
Current liabilities			
Common shares			
Retained earnings			
Total liabilities and equity			

Analysis component:

_____
_____
_____
_____
_____
_____
_____
_____
_____
_____
_____
_____
_____
_____
_____
_____
_____
_____
_____
_____
_____
_____
_____
_____
_____
_____
_____

Transaction	Current Assets	Quick Assets	Current Liabilities	Current Ratio	Quick Ratio	Working Capital

(a) Current ratio:
_____
_____
_____
_____

(b) Quick ratio:
_____
_____
_____
_____

(c) Days' sales uncollected:
_____
_____
_____
_____

(d) Inventory turnover:
_____
_____
_____
_____

(e) Days' sales in inventory:
_____
_____
_____
_____

(f) Ratio of pledged assets to secured liabilities:
_____
_____
_____
_____

(g) Times interest earned:
_____
_____
_____
_____

(h) Profit margin:
_____
_____
_____
_____

(i) Total asset turnover:
_____
_____
_____
_____

(j) Return on total assets:

_____
_____
_____

(k) Return on common shareholders' equity:

_____
_____
_____
_____

Problem 17-6A

Part 1

a.

Book value per common share	Book value per preferred share

b.

Book value per common share	Book value per preferred share

Part 2

c.

Book value per common share	Book value per preferred share

d.

Book value per common share	Book value per preferred share

Name _____

ALBERTA PLAYGROUND
Common-Size Comparative Balance Sheet
As at March 31, 2017 and March 31, 2016

	2017	2016

ALBERTA PLAYGROUND INC
Common-Size Comparative Income Statement
Years Ending March 31, 2017 and March 31, 2016

	2017	2016

Part 2

Ratio	Calculation	Favourable (F) or Unfavourable (U)
Current ratio		
Total asset turnover		
Debt ratio		
Equity ratio		
Times interest earned		
Profit margin		
Return on total assets		
Earnings per share		

Analysis component:

_____
_____
_____
_____
_____
_____
_____
_____
_____
_____

Problem 17-8A

	2017	2016	Change	Comparison to Industry Average
Current ratio	1.08:1	0.97:1		
Quick ratio	0.99:1	0.84:1		
Accounts receivable turnover	16	18		
Days' sales uncollected	35	31		
Inventory turnover	6	7		
Days' sales in inventory	49	37		
Total asset turnover	3.2	1.8		
Debt ratio	67	47		
Times interest earned	2.2	6.3		
Profit margin	15	18		
Gross profit ratio	17	16		

MODERN HEALTH INC.
Income Statement Trends
For Years Ended December 31, 2011–2017

	2017	*2016*	*2015*	*2014*	*2013*	*2012*	*2011*
Net sales							
Cost of goods sold							
Operating expenses							
Profit before taxes							

MODERN HEALTH INC.
Balance Sheet Trends
December 31, 2011–2017

	2017	*2016*	*2015*	*2014*	*2013*	*2012*	*2011*
Cash							
Accounts receivable, net							
Inventory							
Other current assets							
Investments							
Plant and equip., net							
Total assets							
Current liabilities							
Non-current liabilities							
Common shares							
Retained earnings							
Total liabilities and equity							

Analysis component:

_____
_____
_____
_____
_____
_____
_____
_____
_____
_____
_____
_____
_____
_____
_____
_____
_____
_____

Name _____

1. Current ratio:	**2017**	**2016**	**2015**

2.

ORGANIC GROCERY CORPORATION
Common-Size Comparative Income Statement
For Years Ended December 31, 2017, 2016, and 2015

	2017	*2016*	*2015*
Net sales			
Cost of goods sold			
Gross profit from sales			
Selling expenses			
Administrative expenses			
Total expenses			
Profit before taxes			
Income taxes			
Profit			

3.

ORGANIC GROCERY CORPORATION
Balance Sheet Data in Trend Percentages
December 31, 2017, 2016, and 2015

	2017	*2016*	*2015*
Assets			
Current assets			
Investments			
Plant and equipment			
Total assets			
Liabilities and Equity			
Current liabilities			
Common shares			
Retained earnings			
Total liabilities and equity			

Analysis component:

_____
_____
_____
_____
_____
_____
_____
_____
_____
_____
_____
_____
_____
_____
_____
_____
_____
_____
_____
_____
_____
_____
_____
_____

Transaction	Current Assets	Quick Assets	Current Liabilities	Current Ratio	Quick Ratio	Working Capital

Name _____

_____
_____
_____
_____
_____
_____
_____
_____
_____
_____
_____
_____
_____
_____
_____
_____
_____
_____
_____
_____
_____
_____
_____
_____
_____
_____
_____

Problem 17-5B   Part 1

	2017	2016	F/U
Quick ratio			
Inventory turnover			
Accounts payable turnover			
Debt ratio			

	2017	**2016**	**F/U**
Ratio of pledged assets to secured liabilities			
Times interest earned			
Profit margin			
Return on total assets			
Book value per common share			

Part 2

	2017	**2016**	**2015**	**2014**
Net sales				100.00
Cost of goods sold				100.00
Gross profit				100.00
Operating expenses				100.00
Operating profit				100.00
Interest expense				100.00
Profit before taxes				100.00
Income taxes				100.00
Profit				100.00

Analysis component: _____

_____

_____

_____

_____

_____

_____

_____

_____

_____

_____

_____
_____
_____
_____
_____
_____
_____
_____
_____
_____
_____
_____
_____
_____

Problem 17-6B

Part 1

a.

Book value per common share	Book value per preferred share

b.

Book value per common share	Book value per preferred share

Part 2

c.

Book value per common share	Book value per preferred share

d.

Book value per common share	Book value per preferred share

Name _____

ECO PLAY LTD
Balance Sheet
As at December 31
(in thousands of dollars)

	2017	2016

Fundamental Accounting Principles, 15ce, Working Papers

ECO PLAY LTD
Income Statement
For the years ended December 31
(in thousands of dollars)

	2017	2016

_____
_____
_____
_____

Part 2

Ratio	Calculation	Favourable (F) or Unfavourable (U)
Current ratio		
Accounts receivable turnover		
Inventory turnover		
Accounts payable turnover		
Debt ratio		
Gross profit ratio		
Return on total assets		
Earnings per share		

Analysis component:

_____
_____
_____
_____
_____
_____
_____
_____

Problem 17-8B

	2017	2016	Trend	Comparison to Industry Average
Current ratio	1.14:1	1.23:1		
Quick ratio	1.00:1	0.99:1		
Accounts receivable turnover	11	9		
Days' sales uncollected	26	29		
Inventory turnover	4.2	3.7		
Days' sales in inventory	63	67		
Total asset turnover	1.8	2.0		
Debt ratio	35	44		
Times interest earned	45	44		
Profit margin	11	9		
Gross profit ratio	14	15		